COMING FULL CIRCLE

Healing Trauma Using Psychedelics

Shannon Duncan

PRESENT MOMENT
——— PRESS ———
ACTUALLY HELPFUL SELF-HELP
2358 University Ave., Unit 591
San Diego, CA 92104

Library of Congress Cataloging-in-Publication Data
Names: Duncan, Shannon, 1970- author.
Title: Coming full circle : healing trauma using psychedelics /
               Shannon Duncan.
Description: San Diego, CA : Present Moment Press, [2023]
Identifiers: ISBN: 9781959254041
Subjects: LCSH: Hallucinogenic drugs--Therapeutic use. | Post-
               traumatic stress disorder--Alternative treatment. | Psychic
               trauma--Alternative treatment. | Traumatic incident reduction--
               Alternative treatment. | Victims of violent crimes--Psychological
               aspects--Alternative treatment. | Mind and body therapies. |
               Stress management. | Change (Psychology) | LCGFT: Self-help
               publications.
Classification: LCC: RM324.8 .D86 2023 | DDC: 615.7/883--dc23

Printed in USA

ISBN: 978-1-959254-04-1

1   2   3   4   5   6   7   8   9   10

The Legal Mumbo Jumbo

NOTICE TO THE CONSUMER

This book presents the author's experiments and explorations with various psychedelic substances, including but not limited to MDMA, psilocybin mushrooms, 3-MMC, Ketamine and 5-MeO-DMT (collectively "psychedelics").

It is a criminal offense in the United States and in many other countries, punishable by imprisonment and/or fines to manufacture, purchase, sell, possess, or supply psychedelics. The FDA has not approved psychedelics for medical uses outside of clinical trials and government-sponsored research. They are Schedule I illegal substances under the federal Controlled Substances Act. Simple possession of them is a violation of federal law as well as laws in many states. Nothing contained in this book is intended to encourage or support illegal behavior.

You should understand that this book is meant to present the author's experiences only and is not intended to encourage you to break any laws. No attempt should be made to use these substances for any purpose except in a legally sanctioned clinical trial.* Notwithstanding the legality or illegality of the author's descriptions of his association with psychedelics, no attempt at self-diagnosis or self-treatment for long-term mental or emotional problems should be made without first consulting a qualified medical practitioner.

*Currently many new centers for psychedelics research have been launched, including the Centre for Psychedelic Research at Imperial College London, the UC Berkeley Center for the Science of Psychedelics, the Center for Psychedelic and Consciousness Research at Johns Hopkins University, the Center for Psychedelic Research and Therapy at Dell Medical School at the University of Texas at Austin, the Center for Psychedelic Psychotherapy and Trauma Research at the Icahn School of Medicine at Mount Sinai, the Psychae Institute in Melbourne, and Multidisciplinary Association for Psychedelic Studies (https://maps.org) (MAPS), a leader in psychedelic research and therapy.

This book is dedicated to those who have given
so much of themselves in order to help me find
my way to authentic emotional healing.

And, it is dedicated to those who are courageously
forging a path towards their own healing.

COMING FULL CIRCLE

Contents

The Road Ahead

Many people are hearing about the potential of psychedelics to help heal emotional trauma and are curious if it might be the right approach for them. I have healed deeply and benefited in amazing ways from using psychedelics for this purpose and know others who have as well. There is much more to this than you might imagine, and I'm here to guide you through the necessary understandings so you can begin to make an informed decision about whether this approach is right for you or not.

There is so much I learned along the way that I wished that I could have known before I started, which is why I wrote this book. I feel sharing what I've been through and what I've learned could be of genuine service to those also considering this path towards healing.

It's been more than twenty years since I wrote my first book, *Present Moment Awareness*, in which I described the evolution my life took as I learned to be more aware of myself in the present moment. By simply slowing down and paying attention as my body and mind interpreted the life happening around me, I was able to face my insecurities and fears — and this allowed me to grow. In looking back at where I'd come from, I could see that this process had brought about a massive improvement in my experience of life.

But that old saying, *You don't know what you don't know*, rang just as true then as it does today. I could only see my life from the context I was inhabiting at the time. I had no sense of how much farther it was possible to go in personal growth. And to be completely up front, I still have no real idea how much farther it is possible to go. What I can say with absolute certainty is that if I took five big steps forward in my growth during the time leading up to my first book, then I've taken twenty-five steps in the last few years of dedicated, guided psychedelic therapeutic work.

As you will see, this book is part memoir and part informative guide, structured as a journey we'll take together to learn about all of this in much the same way I did, building up crucial understandings as we go.

The memoir aspects of what I've written here are intensely personal, and they are difficult for me to share. I'm an introvert by nature and a very private person. Many times, I tried to talk myself out of sharing so much about myself, usually in the middle of the night as I was wide awake, gripping the sheets and staring at the ceiling for hours. But ultimately, I decided I must set aside my fears of being so exposed and go for it if this material was going to be genuinely helpful. Understanding what brought me to using psychedelics therapeutically in this specific way makes it possible to understand the process I've gone through to heal and how it works. It's important to have a sense of me and why I went through all of this so you can begin to consider it within the context of your own life.

This Book Is Divided into Three Key Parts

Part One lays the foundation for understanding both using psychedelics to heal and what brought me to the point of using psychedelics in this specialized way. There are a lot of misconceptions and misinformation about how psychedelics can be used for healing, which I hope to dispel to provide you with an unflinching, realistic understanding of what this really looks like.

Part Two takes a deep dive into the guided psychedelic healing process. We'll talk about the professionals who guide the sessions and keep you safe, how to prepare for taking one of these journeys, and what to know about navigating the experience to get the most from it. Last, we'll talk about the time of healing after a psychedelic session, the *integration period*, and how to get the most benefits.

Part Three is where everything we've covered so far comes together for my own story, and possibly for yours as well. By this time, you should know in your bones whether or not you feel this is right for you to pursue further.

Words of Hope and Caution

Psychedelics are powerful in ways you might not even begin to suspect, even if you've used them recreationally many times. They can not only pose a danger to your physical health if misused, but they can also open doors to your inner world that can put you into challenging emotional and psychological states if you are unprepared or don't have the proper support. And those emotions don't just come up on the day you use the psychedelics, but can continue to do so for days or weeks afterwards. So please, carefully take your time to seek qualified guidance before proceeding with any kind of therapeutic use of psychedelics.

I'm not a medical professional and I cannot possibly know your personal history, your psychological or emotional health, your tolerance for taking substances of any kind, what kind of support you have available to you, or anything else about you at all. With that understanding, you can see that I cannot possibly know if this is the right approach to healing for you.

Everyone must take responsibility to figure out for themselves whether using psychedelics to heal is right for them or not. But you must not use my opinions here as the only basis for that decision. I want so much for you to find a path to healing that truly works for you in a safe and supported way. In my case, as you'll see later, I knew from the core of my being that using psychedelics towards this end was going to be right for me. You'll have to come to that knowing for yourself and in your own way.

Much of the trauma I was desperate to heal had been locked away deep inside, inaccessible in spite of decades of various forms of talk therapy, hypnotherapy, meditation, typical psychedelic use, and myriad other approaches. In my carefully weighed judgment, it was worth it for me to do this psychedelic work under the vigilant guidance of professionals. I did this to give myself the opportunity to allow heavily defended, traumatized aspects of myself the chance to finally, truly heal.

Just as I have had to do, if you are considering using any psychedelic, it is important you educate yourself on any health, safety, and legal concerns, and make an informed decision from there. My understanding is that those with mental health issues like bipolar disorder or schizophrenia, and especially those on psychiatric drugs, should never take psychedelics. If you have a family history of neurologically based mental health issues, you should do your research to make an informed decision before using psychedelics for any reason.

Many who consider healing with psychedelics have concerns about addiction. None of the psychedelics that I describe using in this book are physically addictive like heroin, cocaine or prescription opioids can be. The one exception here is ketamine. But that possible addiction is psychological, not physical, and seems to happen mostly with those who use it for chronic pain management or during excessive recreational use. Nevertheless, all of these medicines are incredibly powerful in their own ways and must be treated with a great deal of respect and an abundance of caution. None are meant to provide a place to hide, but rather to open the doors within that allow true healing to be possible.

And, of course, in the United States and many other countries psychedelics are illegal. Some cities or states within the United States have decriminalized some psychedelics at the time of this writing, but they are currently still illegal at the federal level. Just know that attempting to obtain or possessing any of these substances could potentially have significant legal consequences.

Last, this book contains frank discussions about child abuse, trauma, and the devastating ways that it can show up in a person's life. For some, this might be deeply disturbing, triggering their own unhealed emotional wounds from trauma. It's important to be aware of this and to view anything triggered not as a setback, but rather as an opportunity to explore, learn, and heal.

Part One

One can choose to go back toward safety or forward toward growth.
Growth must be chosen again and again;
fear must be overcome again and again.

— ABRAHAM MASLOW

CHAPTER 1

PSYCHEDELICS

We commonly use a variety of chemicals to alter our experience of life, from caffeine in the morning to be more alert, to painkillers to soothe aches and pains, to alcohol or marijuana to relax or be more open. Psychedelics evoke a *very* different kind of experience.

For many people who haven't had any personal experience of them, psychedelics bring to mind images of unwashed hippies at music festivals or eccentric weirdos talking about far-out stuff. And sure, there's a grain of truth there, although the media framed those images for the uninitiated masses from a place of ignorance and fear. In reality, a whole generation was shaking off the shackles of a deeply repressive social mindset, and only the most extreme and cartoonish examples were reported to the public.

In truth, psychedelics have been used as tools for entering non-ordinary states of consciousness for thousands of years. In various cultures, shamans, medicine men and women, priests, and elders have used psychedelics spiritually for rites of initiation, ceremonies, vision quests, and as a tool for obtaining a higher perspective, knowledge, and growth. Historically, people have been tripping out and enjoying the inner spectacle and adventure created by psychedelics for a very, very long time.

Somewhere along the way, the use of such powerful substances fell out of favor in most societies and was made illegal, largely owing to those in power fearing what it might do to the carefully managed control they held over those they governed. I won't get into the whole War on Drugs and "Just Say No" campaigns, other than to say that such efforts have been a horrible waste of money and lives with no measurable results other than empowering the growth of immense networks of organized crime and countless lives wasted away in prisons. There are much better ways than brute force, violence, and stealing people's freedoms to manage drug use. And no authority has the right to control what people do in their own hearts and minds. It is absurd that drugs as damaging as cigarettes and alcohol are legal and readily available through convenient and regulated retail sources, but psychedelics can land a person in prison.

These campaigns may have started based on real concerns about the epidemic of easily abused and addictive substances that were destroying lives, families, and communities. But they were severely misguided in their execution. The flawed and often outright dishonest propaganda that was used to scare the public into compliance led to radical misunderstandings about all drugs, their users, and their abuse.

It's important to note that around this same time SSRI (selective serotonin reuptake inhibitor) antidepressants, with their massive economic potential, were just getting a foothold in the market. The appearance of these drugs was considerable motivation to shut down any research on psychedelics that might potentially help patients heal relatively quickly, instead of having to pay for antidepressants for a lifetime.

It's common for people, especially Americans, to have deeply ingrained misconceptions and strong feelings about "drugs" (medicines not prescribed by a doctor). Even people who have themselves experienced profound changes in their lives due to healing with psychedelics can continue to cling to these misguided notions out of habit. The indoctrination of the propaganda around drugs has its claws deep in most of us, and it can be hard to know to even question those beliefs unless someone points out the conflict.

Slowly and painfully, researchers are once more gaining permission from their governments to work with psychedelics legally. This research is beginning to demonstrate psychedelics' incredible ability, when properly used, to help heal mental and emotional health issues. Real progress is being made. But until patients have access to competent and qualified legal outlets, there are true heroes I call *psychedelic guides*. These risk much, including potential legal entanglements and even their freedom, to offer guided psychedelic medicine therapies. Their drive to be of true service to others is inspirational, and my heart absolutely breaks with gratitude that they persevere.

WHAT IS A PSYCHEDELIC DRUG?

A psychedelic drug is a hallucinogen that triggers a *non-ordinary state of consciousness* — what pop culture calls "tripping." Among friends, it's not uncommon to look at one another during a big experience and say, *Oh man, I'm tripping balls!* And for someone who has never been in a psychedelic-induced altered state of consciousness, it's not just difficult to wrap your head around what that must be like, it's impossible. The best description of trying to explain the psychedelic experience I've heard is that it's like trying to explain the color blue to someone who has been blind since birth. It's simply so far outside of any known experience for them that it's not describable.

It's known that psychedelics predominantly interact with the serotonin mechanisms of the brain and that they cause the brain to activate, use and connect different areas than during the normal waking state. Outside of that, it's not well understood exactly how psychedelics induce altered states of consciousness.

Insights

Never believe quotes that you find on the internet.

— ABRAHAM LINCOLN

Most equate their psychedelic experiences with trippy visuals, deep thoughts and insights — moments of clarity when you see aspects of yourself or your life from a different point of view. If you tell a person who has tripped before that you took psychedelics, they will almost inevitably ask you about any insights you might have gained. Even if you've used psychedelics purely recreationally, you almost certainly recall having many *wow!* moments when some aspect of your life was shown to you from a different perspective than you'd normally see it. Such insights always feel like incredible moments of clarity and often can be truly helpful for personal growth and healing.

However, your own rationalizations can at times get in the way of clear insight: you see what you want to see or what you are afraid is true. At other times, what you see shouldn't be taken literally but is symbolic instead. There are many factors that can affect the insights you receive while on a psychedelic journey.

This is why it is important to let things settle for at least a few weeks before making any life-changing decisions based on insights from psychedelic experiences. You certainly wouldn't be the first person to rush out to quit a job, propose marriage, end a relationship, or start the process of moving to a new location after inspiring insights on psychedelics. You would also not be the first to end up regretting it. No matter how important an insight might feel, if it's right, it'll still be right in a couple of weeks or months. Any urgency to take immediate action is a big red flag telling you that careful, sober consideration is most definitely needed.

Adventures in Self-Exploration

My early experiences using psychedelics were always and without fail grand adventures. They were incredibly interesting, sometimes challenging, and I loved them. I especially loved going for long walks or hanging out in nature with a good friend or friends while doing it.

What I loved most about the experiences was the sense of inner exploration and the insights that would light up my brain. I hardly ever used psychedelics purely for the fun of it, although they can indeed be a great deal of fun. Once I had a taste of the honest, self-reflecting nature of psychedelics, of the deeper self-awareness that could grow from their use, my intent in using them, even in a fun setting like a music festival or camping, was always with an eye for personal growth. I'd ask myself: *What will I take back with me from this experience?* I had a sense that there was much more to me than what I had previously realized, and I craved learning what that was.

Decades ago, close friends and I would meet regularly to go on what we called "outings" on psychedelics. We'd venture through my neighborhood or over to the beautiful Balboa Park in San Diego to think deep thoughts and ponder deep ideas with each other. Those were fantastic, beautiful experiences. Whenever I describe them to someone, I can't help but have a huge smile on my face.

Fear and Loathing in a National Park

Kings River runs through Sequoia National Park in central California. Each year I'd go with one of my best friends to camp in the foothills of the park, where we'd spend our days next to the river, alternating between dipping into the ice-cold pools beneath waterfalls and stretching out on huge sun-soaked boulders to dry off. And each year, we would dedicate at least one of those days to having a psychedelic outing, usually on psilocybin mushrooms, or "shrooms."

I remember one visit so clearly. I was gingerly climbing over the boulders and rocks that we had to cross to get to one of our favorite pools. I'd had many months of knee pain that my doctor couldn't figure out or help me with. That day my friend and I each ate around four grams of mushrooms, sipped ice-cold beer, and enjoyed the day. I found myself lying back across a huge, smooth boulder in the middle of the pool, my head hanging over the edge to observe the upside-down stream flowing away from me and losing myself in the sound of the rushing water. As the mushrooms settled in, the boulders turned translucent, revealing their slowly churning liquid cores.

With the universe starting to unravel at the edges, I found myself focusing on the constant presence of the knee pain in my life. Now, in a crazy, profound moment of visualized understanding, of insight, I *saw* and *felt* how tension I was carrying had been keeping my body, especially my back and hips, out of alignment. I didn't *think* this; rather, I knew and could feel the truth of it.

As that understanding sank in, I lay there breathing, just observing, as the recent narrative of my life that I'd been fearing would happen played out in my mind's eye. I'd been constantly fearful that my business would fall apart and I'd be unable to provide for my daughter. This fear had built up to a crippling level in my body.

As I lay on the rock, the fear crept up on me. At first, I'd clench down on my breathing in a misguided attempt to hold the feelings back. But like the pressure of water against a dam, the fear would start to build and feel overwhelming. I desperately wanted to escape it, but I knew deep down that running away wouldn't work. Instead I focused on my breath, doing my best to surrender. None of my feelings felt too big to be endured, as long as they were flowing in and out with my breath. Over and over again, I felt the waves of fear flowing through and out of me, and I came to experience them as nothing more than energy flowing, until at last, I came to a point of peace and was able to relax deeply.

At the end of the day, when we were packing up to go back to our camp, I felt like one of those huge boulders around us had been lifted off my shoulders, and, incredibly, I walked with no knee pain whatsoever. At least fifteen years later, as of this writing, that pain has never returned.

Personal Growth

It was on another outing, this time on MDMA (more commonly known as Ecstasy), as a friend and I were walking through the neighborhoods near my home and talking, when I had the first experience that I could ever remember of feeling love and approval for myself. I was in my late twenties and never even knew that it was missing from my life until it hit me then, like a bolt of lightning.

As with any time I had a profound insight, I carefully observed how it felt in my body, so I could work on feeling into it again later. Of course, I closed up again to the feeling after the drug wore off, but whereas before I never knew that people could feel this way about themselves, now I had a new map of what was possible and a *felt sense* of the direction I needed to move in.

This insight showed me a new perspective and was a life-changing gift for me. And while this experience was incredibly powerful, what I didn't know at that time was that it only scratched the surface of the kind of healing that is possible with psychedelics. A deeper, intentional exploration with psychedelics would have led to the expression of the pain of a lifetime of emotional isolation and my desperation for real connection. It would have revealed a clear understanding of how it was the felt sense of shame for even existing that kept those loving feelings towards myself locked away so deep inside. This is the true power of using psychedelics to heal.

CHAPTER 2

THE DIFFERENT USES FOR PSYCHEDELICS

There are three fundamental types of experiences that psychedelics are used for. The first two are the most common and well known. I will refer to them as *recreational* and *expansive.*

Recreational use is when psychedelics are taken for the trippy experience that is meant to be exciting, adventurous, weird, wild, and most of all, fun. It can also be a deep bonding experience — and don't even get me started on the incredible intensity that it can add to sex! Taking psychedelics at music festivals and concerts, when hanging out with friends, camping, on long walks, etc., are all examples of recreational psychedelic experiences.

Using psychedelics in this way can add an amazing new dimension to personal experiences that can often end up being educational and healing all on its own. Many people have had recreational trips that have spontaneously evolved into profound spiritual experiences or moments of deep personal growth.

Expansive use is about intentionally using psychedelics for personal development, spiritual growth and healing. These kinds of experiences are intended to help you expand into something greater than yourself and gain a higher perspective. The vast majority of my early experiences with psychedelics fell into this category, even when I was in a recreational, fun setting.

An expansive experience can engender profound shifts and changes in how you perceive, and thus in how you think and feel about yourself and your experience of life. Expansive experiences can bring about spiritual awakenings that reshape a person's relationship to God, the universe, or whatever their sense of a higher power happens to be. Many people have had deeply meaningful, life-affirming and life-changing insights come to them during expansive experiences, whether they were alone, communing with friends, gathering in a group, out in nature, with a spiritual teacher, or even in psychedelic therapy.

For anyone striving to heal, an expansive experience would likely be a great place to start. For many, if not most, the experience would be more than they ever could have imagined and will give them everything that they are yearning for from psychedelics.

The third, rarely suspected, usually misunderstood, and often misidentified psychedelic experience is what I call *medicine work*, and it is fundamentally different from the other two.

Recreational and expansive uses both have a singular focus on a positive, mind-expanding experience. But if your goal is to deeply heal and evolve, the experience can also be so much more than that. Insights are to psychedelics as sweating is to exercise — it's just what happens when you do it.

But ultimately, no matter how big the trip is, it is still splashing in the shallow end of the pool compared to what is actually possible for growth and healing at the most fundamental levels of who and what you are with medicine work.

Psychedelics for Deep Healing

Before we continue, I want to be clear that nothing I'm saying here is meant in *any* way to diminish the life-changing, heart-opening, spiritually blossoming experiences that anyone has had on psychedelics. I've had many of these kinds of experiences and cherish them with immense gratitude. They were the stepping stones that brought me to where I am today, and I fully hope to have more of those experiences in the future.

Medicine work, however, serves a distinctly different purpose than recreational or expansive psychedelic usage. As with a Swiss Army knife, you pull out the tool you need for the task at hand. Medicine work is about going deep into an authentic, direct experience of yourself, and the felt sense of the psychedelics is a side effect, not the point.

Medicine work is all about *intentionally* going deep, very deep, to effect healing far beyond what expansive insights can give. I'm taking such pains to clarify this distinction because there are limits to what expansive experiences can do for you, and most people I've spoken to about it, including many calling themselves psychedelic guides, have had no idea that more is even possible.

In medicine work, psychedelics are viewed as powerful tools to help you realize specific goals in specialized ways. They are keys that unlock the subterranean spaces within you where traumas live in the darkness. When psychedelics are truly used *as* medicine — and not just *called* medicine — it is almost always a big, messy, challenging, sometimes fearful, and ultimately deeply rewarding experience.

Intuitively, I always know that medicine work is going to take me into places that I'm emotionally programmed to stay out of. It's scary in the same way that going skydiving for the first time is scary; the fear is instinctive. I've often been terrified as I was preparing to take the medicine to start a journey. At times, it's taken all my courage just to not run away. This instinctive response is how I know my intentions for the journey are pointing me in the right direction, and that they are sincere. Using psychedelics as a medicine is radically different from using the exact same dosage of the same drug in any other way. You have to be willing to let the experience, the medicine, go wherever it needs to go to facilitate the growth and healing that you are being called to.

In a recreational or expansive experience, ego defenses keep most hidden, scary, emotional material from being felt, just as they do in everyday life. This is why recreational or expansive experiences are usually fun and introspective. There can sometimes be challenging feelings or fear that you must pass through with breathing and relaxing, but the ego's controls over deep, scary emotions are pretty much as functional as they always are. And yet at the same time, you can have more access to positive experiences like joy, elation, love, connection, wonder and awe.

In medicine work, though, the felt sense of the experience expands out into the entire body, especially waking up in the abdominal region, solar plexus and around the heart. This is where most emotion is felt and where we normally clamp down on it to stop the feeling when it seems overwhelming. It's in those regions that muscular tensions tend to lock down on old pains and traumas to prevent them from being reexperienced.

Opening to the full range of those deep physical sensations of emotion is at the heart of doing medicine work. You simply can't know the difference until you've experienced it because it works in direct opposition to deeply ingrained, largely unconscious, psychological defense mechanisms.

Ego Death

Large doses of some psychedelics can push you into a state of *ego death*, which can be an intense and liberating experience as the ego's control is briefly suspended. This, too, is a different experience from intentional medicine work. Doses big enough to cause ego death are experienced like bombs being dropped. Something is going to happen for sure, and it's likely to be profound.

The sudden changes or improvements in my experience of life that often follow ego death experiences tend to fade away over the coming days or weeks. There is benefit for sure, but I usually view these temporary reprieves as showing what is possible, rather than trying to cling to them desperately as they recede.

Medicine work is an intentional exploration and involves facing fears and difficult feelings. True, honest intentions you set going into the medicine work session are followed with precision and can take you deep into your shadow realms. The changes that accumulate over time can be lasting, permanent changes. We'll discuss intentions in more detail later in the book.

Bad Trips

There are times when recreational or expansive psychedelic experiences can bring challenging emotions rushing to the surface. If the person experiencing this is lucky enough to have the proper mindset and support, they can process these emotions and start healing right then and there.

More often, however, when challenging emotions come up during a recreational or expansive journey, the experience is called a "bad trip." This is because the person experiencing it isn't prepared for the intensity of the fear that can come up.

They've unintentionally slipped into deep, emotional material that is usually locked away. And without the proper context and support to help manage the experience, it can be overwhelming and terrifying. The mind can spin off into paranoia or into imagining terrible scenarios in order to have a place to focus that fear without having to encounter the actual emotions trying to emerge that are causing it. The common wisdom is to keep breathing, stay calm, and remind yourself that you are on a drug that will wear off soon. And that's really good advice, unless your goal is one of deep healing.

You might blow off some steam on a trip and cry, vomit, or release pent-up emotions in some way, and afterwards this can feel great. And you can have unbelievable spiritual openings so blissful that no words can ever begin to describe your experience.

But none of that is the same as a deeply cathartic expression of past trauma that has been held onto out of the unconscious fear of having to feel it. This is when it can get really intense, when feelings come up that your ego is hardwired to protect you from experiencing at all costs. Such experience is the realm of medicine work — *not blowing off steam, but healing the source of the "heat" that creates that steam.*

Those experiences perceived as "bad trips" in typical psychedelic journeys are the pay dirt we are looking for in medicine work. Those feelings are your gateway to go deeper. In a medicine work journey, you are prepared for these kinds of experiences and have an honest intention to surrender, embrace, and keep breathing through the expression of these emotions as well as any fear protecting them from being felt. A good psychedelic guide will keep you breathing, relaxing, and anchored in your body as an observer.

I took eight grams of mushrooms in a medicine work session (three grams is considered by most to be a big dose) and never noticed any psychedelic visuals the entire time. Rather, it was all tsunamis of pent-up emotional energy roiling through me to be released.

My emotional defenses were on high alert, trying to protect me from experiencing feelings that had been locked away for reasons that must have seemed important at the time. My mind kept trying to take over, to think my way through it — which is just another form of trying to escape. The key was to keep surrendering to the physicality of the experience, to be a loving witness and allow the feelings to be expressed and felt, deeply and completely, even if I didn't understand what they were, where they were coming from, or what they might mean.

My medicine guide was connected to me the entire time, reminding me to breathe from deep in my abdomen, to stay connected to my body. Had I been alone, or had she not been so qualified to work with trauma and so experienced in her own deep healing work, I could have been in a bad place, alone in mind-breaking terror with no way to escape. But as it was, staying with my breath and connected to the physical sensations of the experience, my mind didn't generate meaning about the fear. Instead, that energy was able to flow through me instead of being dammed up by resistance and rising to intolerable levels.

As I started coming down, I spent two hours shouting as loudly as I possibly could. Not screaming, just releasing energy through shouting whatever profanities or frustrations wanted to come through me. It felt incredible afterwards, but my throat was so raw, I could barely speak for days. I have heart-crushing gratitude for every second of the experience.

Even if you aren't specifically processing trauma, it is common that pent-up emotional energy can be released in expansive psychedelic healing work or medicine work. There are perspectives and beliefs about the self and our worth that, upon a complete and honest inspection in the light of our conscious awareness, can be let go and release years, even decades, of unexpressed sadness, anger, frustration, despair, or loneliness.

I've often heard people say, *I don't have deep stuff to process*, when it's clear in just speaking with them that they most certainly do. Avoiding looking at "deep stuff" and thus feeling those feelings is one of the ego's prime directives. But it is this kind of healing that so many are looking for, even if they can't articulate it specifically. It opens you to a new perspective from which you view yourself and your life. It's true, authentic growth that once earned cannot be taken away.

Recreational Use During Medicine Work

Many seem to find that once they begin working with psychedelics for healing, other uses can become problematic. This can be especially true if they are working through issues involving past trauma.

Once you set a clear intention in your medicine work that you want the experience to open you deeply, to help you give expression to those hidden and defended aspects of yourself, to express and release deeply held pain or fear or sadness, to heal, then that is what the psychedelics often tend to do, no matter the situation that they are taken in.

Once you have started engaging in medicine work, using psychedelics recreationally can easily slide you into a medicine work state, but without the protections and support that are part of an intentional medicine work journey. Even if your past psychedelic experiences were all enjoyable, you can now easily find yourself in bad trip territory without the safety of a controlled, contained space or a skilled and qualified guide.

This happened to me once when a woman I was seeing asked to have her first psychedelic experiences with me. I was excited to show her the potential in this alternate universe. We initially tried MDMA recreationally together, and it was a lovely day of sharing and connection. But the next time she requested an outing, we did mushrooms together, and her initial fear of the feeling of the mushrooms coming on triggered in me a deep fear that escalated quickly, coming close to real panic.

My thoughts were caught in a loop of, *If I lose my shit, I can't help her if she loses her shit.* In all my many previous recreational and expansive outings, I had never experienced any big, unmanageable fear like this from mushrooms, so I hadn't even considered that it could happen now outside of a medicine work session.

The intensity of emotions I was experiencing was common and manageable in guided medicine work. But here, without any container or support, I was right on the edge of panic. That poor woman heard me vomiting, saw me lying there with my legs twitching uncontrollably and heard me laughing maniacally. Basically, she got to see how the sausage gets made with medicine work and wasn't digging it, and I couldn't possibly blame her for that.

Luckily, my sage advice to her beforehand had been that if things ever got difficult, the key was to get comfortable and focus on deep breathing. This is what she, and not I, did for a few hours until we started coming down. Even now, I still cringe at the memory. I'd promised to keep an eye on her and have an amazing day and had instead learned an important lesson in trying to do recreational outings while still in the process of doing medicine work.

Once old fear or pain starts to be intentionally loosened through medicine work, it will take any opportunity, especially when you use psychedelics, to continue working its way out towards full expression and healing.

CHAPTER 3

MEDICINAL PSYCHEDELICS

There are a lot of psychedelic drug options for doing medicine work. Each has unique qualities that can bring a variety of benefits and challenges. I'll discuss the ones I have used in medicine work. This way when I mention them later in the book, you'll be familiar enough to know what I'm talking about. There are some drugs, like LSD, that I have used many times recreationally and expansively but have not yet used in medicine work, so I don't discuss them here.

What follows is a general overview based on my experiences and is not meant to give complete information about any of these substances. In the heartfelt interest of harm reduction, I'll say it again:

It is *your* responsibility to be fully informed on any psychedelic you consider taking in order to come to an educated decision about whether or not to take it.

I've listed these in the order that it would be most common to encounter them in medicine work, from the easiest experiences to the most challenging. It can be confusing to know what to take or how much; this is why educating yourself is so important. And if you are doing medicine work, then you'll work with your qualified professional guide to find the right psychedelic medicines for you.

MDMA

MDMA is more commonly known as Ecstasy, E, X, Adam, or Molly. MDMA is the psychedelic most people use when starting medicine work because there is little chance of fear becoming an issue during the session. Recreationally, MDMA can be incredibly euphoric and enjoyable. As a medicine, it can give access to deep, painful, or even terrifying memories and emotions in a way that feels manageable and safe. This is why MDMA is frequently used for the treatment of post-traumatic stress disorder (PTSD), which is usually caused by a single or short-lived traumatic event, and Complex PTSD, which shares many symptoms with PTSD but is caused by long-term exposure to repeated trauma such as childhood or spousal abuse and other forms of trauma.

MDMA is a "designer drug," in that it was made in a lab and is both a stimulant and a psychedelic. It is considered an *empathogen*, which means that it increases tactile sensation and creates euphoric feelings that enable the user to feel safe and to be more open with themselves and with others.

MDMA is also incredible for personal and relationship growth in that it enables much greater access to one's own feelings and deep empathy for others. Cognitive biases can be set aside, and more honest communication can happen. Marriages and relationships have been saved, or peacefully ended, by couples working through their issues with the help of MDMA.

It should also be mentioned that MDMA isn't a truth serum. While people using MDMA may not be deceptive out of fear, they can unthinkingly manipulate the conversation and say what the other wants to hear to keep the feelings of deep emotional connection going. The connection becomes everything. This is another reason why working under professional guidance is recommended.

Like all psychedelics, MDMA has risks, but I believe they can all be managed if approached with care. People taking antidepressants like SSRIs (which regulate uptake of the brain chemical serotonin) who also take MDMA can develop a condition called *serotonin syndrome*, which can be fatal. And the common, over-the-counter supplement 5-HTP, which is a precursor your body uses to make serotonin, shouldn't be taken in the few days before taking MDMA, as it may block MDMA's ability to work and can bring about serotonin syndrome as well.

MDMA triggers a massive release of the neurotransmitters serotonin, dopamine, and norepinephrine and blocks the brain's ability to reabsorb them, which keeps those chemicals flooding your brain. Serotonin is a big part of what helps regulate your mood, and when this flood of it is released in your brain, you feel unbelievably happy, open, hopeful, and willing to connect.

When you are low on serotonin, you can naturally feel sad or depressed, and since what goes up must come down, the days following MDMA use can be challenging as your body often doesn't have, or cannot process, the serotonin needed to generate your regular everyday feelings of happiness. This is normal, and you need to be prepared for it so that feeling a bit sad or down after MDMA use isn't taken out of context and mistakenly associated with other events or people in your life.

Because of MDMA's significant stimulant effects, most users tend to clench their jaws, which is known as "gurning." It's not unusual to have a stiff, sore jaw for days after using it. I've found that taking big doses of a good quality magnesium citrate supplement, which is a natural muscle relaxer, dramatically reduces my jaw clenching during a session, and my jaw is much less sore in the days following.

Another important thing to note about MDMA is the *comedown*, when the drug starts wearing off and you start coming back to your normal state. It feels like taking a step down from the high, like a wave suddenly flowing out and then slowly rising again, but not as high as before, over and over again.

This continues until you are completely down from the high. For some people, this stepping down can be difficult. The feelings of openness and connectedness are there one moment and gone the next. There can be feelings of loss and sadness, but such feelings don't last long.

For others, including myself, the feelings evoked by the comedown can even be emotionally painful. During my early experiences, the comedown felt like getting bad news, like the pain in your gut when you've just learned someone you know has died. Blessedly, this never lasted very long.

In my earlier recreational or expansive usage, I would try to escape this comedown feeling in any way I could. A small hit of marijuana could mellow the comedown considerably. Or taking some LSD or mushrooms with the MDMA would greatly reduce the comedown feelings, if I felt them at all. But later, in medicine work, I learned to embrace the comedown effect as an opportunity to heal. Like any triggered reactivity, it was an opportunity, a gateway to go deeper, learn, and heal.

Psilocybin Mushrooms

Psilocybin is the psychoactive ingredient of psychedelic mushrooms, also known as magic mushrooms, mushrooms, or simply shrooms. Mushrooms have been held sacred and used by people to alter their states of consciousness for thousands of years. Lately, they have been getting a lot of attention in research studies for their potential use in healing depression and other emotional and psychological challenges. The fact that this psychedelic is moving into the mainstream is promising.

One of the most popular and easily accessible recreational psychedelics, mushrooms give an intense visual and introspective experience. Depending on how much is taken, mushrooms can give a variety of experiences. The bigger the dose, the further from your normal everyday state of mind you are taken and the closer you move toward complete ego dissolution. Mushrooms have a deep, dream-like quality and can enable a shift in perspective to give you a profound new view of yourself and your life.

Over the years, I've had many powerful insights about myself and my life while in the peak of a mushroom experience. You see yourself and events in your life from a different perspective that can change how you see them when you are back in your everyday state. These kinds of insights are common on mushrooms and LSD, and I've always found them exciting and humbling.

Mushrooms used in medicine work take on a whole new presence in your psychedelic experience, becoming a tool of cultivation much like a plow. Like a plow, they dig deep, breaking up and turning over the tightly packed soil of your inner world. In the process, a wide variety of thoughts, memories, feelings, and perceptions can come bubbling up into your awareness. This can be a beautiful experience, and it can also be intense at times. Having the proper setting, support and guidance is highly recommended, especially with larger doses.

Mushrooms offer significant benefits in dosages ranging from a microdose (between one-tenth and three-tenths of a gram), where you can't consciously tell that you've even had any, all the way up to megadoses (five grams and above). The most common dosage is in the range of two and one-half to three and one-half grams: this is the dosage where things start to get "trippy" with both visuals and a bodily felt high.

2C-B

2C-B, also known as Nexus, Bromo Mescaline, Venus, or Bees, is a different kind of designer drug. It has some of the empathogenic qualities of MDMA and some of the introspective qualities of mushrooms. It doesn't usually produce strong external visual effects unless you take a larger dose. A standard dose for me is usually in the fifteen-milligram range. 2C-B is extremely dose sensitive. Just a few milligrams can make the difference between a mellow, sensual experience and an overwhelming one in which being functional is out of the question until the drug wears off.

Often, I'll take 2C-B on the downward slope of an MDMA or 3-MMC session. This extends the time I have to do inner work and brings a sharper clarity to the experience, which often brings fresh new perspectives about the emotional release achieved earlier in the day.

3-MMC

3-MMC is also known as metaphedrone, and it's another empathogen. It's a designer drug that in some countries is available as a "research chemical" to buy online. In other places, it's been made illegal. It's often confused with its predecessor, 4-MMC, and only highly specialized testing equipment can even tell them apart. My experience has been that they work nearly identically, and I'll refer to them both as 3-MMC.

I was introduced to 3-MMC by a guide as an alternative to MDMA because of the positive feedback coming from therapeutic use in Canada, where it was being used with good results to help with treatment-resistant trauma. 3-MMC carries all of the same warnings as MDMA, as its action on the body seems to be quite similar. However, it often takes me longer to recover and feel back to normal after using 3-MMC than after MDMA.

3-MMC feels speedier and a bit less euphoric than MDMA. At first glance, it would seem to be increasing the undesirable effect and reducing the desirable effect of MDMA, so why would anyone want to use it in a medicinal fashion? The answer is simple: 3-MMC enables me to have laser-focused access to otherwise unreachable emotional material that even MDMA couldn't help me get to.

I can't emphasize enough that 3-MMC is only recommended for those experienced in medicine work. The journey itself will feel pleasant and safe like an MDMA journey, but navigating it takes experience in the psychedelic space. The days and weeks afterward, known as the *integration period*, can at times be extremely challenging compared to MDMA.

Many of my most painful and brutal-feeling integration periods have been after 3-MMC sessions, as a natural result of my psyche adapting to its altered foundations and my depleted neurochemicals. I knew what was happening and how to handle it, yet I was still surprised at times at the intensity of the emotions bubbling up within me. 3-MMC can open deep emotional material in a direct way, whereas with MDMA you ease towards it layer by layer.

If your honest intention is to directly confront trauma and not shy away from it, 3-MMC can most likely take you there. Just know that its use can destabilize your system, causing emotional havoc until your body figures out how to restructure things to work with the new changes. In my experience, 3-MMC works like nothing else. It is a specialized tool, and I never go into it lightly.

5-MeO-DMT

5-MeO-DMT is thought to be the most potent psychedelic in existence, and I have a true reverence for it. An incredibly small amount of the pure substance vaporized and inhaled can launch you into a state of complete dissociation within a minute. It's also often simply called Five or 5-MeO. When it comes from toad venom, it's called toad.

The 5-MeO-DMT used in medicine work is normally either a pure synthetic lab-made version or a natural version made from the dried venom of the Sonoran Desert toad (also known as the Colorado River toad).

Toad contains a variety of other psychoactive alkaloids, so you have to use more of it by weight than you would a pure synthetic source of 5-MeO-DMT. While you might use fifty milligrams of toad vaporized for a full-release experience, you'd only need around fifteen milligrams of the synthetic version to get the same effect. There is a difference in the feel of the two. To me, toad has a more earthy feel, and the synthetic version has a very clean, clear, and almost clinical feel — not clinical in a cold or bad sense, just very precise with nothing extra. But otherwise, the action is nearly identical.

In my own medicine work, I sometimes vaporize 5-MeO-DMT toad venom but more often use the synthetic in a vape pen. An experience using the vapor lasts around fifteen minutes before you start coming down, and believe me, that often feels like plenty! Occasionally I'll snort synthetic 5-MeO-DMT, which gives a much longer experience that moves at a slower pace. All of these applications have their place in my tool kit, depending on what I'm trying to do.

Three Different Drugs

5-MeO-DMT is actually three different drugs, depending on the amount you use.

In small, barely perceptible doses, it can dramatically help your energy and words to flow in a more traditional therapeutic setting. I've had incredible sessions where one insightful connection leads to the next and to the next and to the next, almost effortlessly.

In moderate doses, you really feel the drug in your body, there is an obvious visual psychedelic experience, and the energy of emotion moves more freely through you, sometimes with big energetic releases. It's unbelievable at helping stuck emotional energy to move.

For many, the experience of moderate doses of 5-MeO-DMT can be overwhelming, like trying to drink from a fire hose. This sense of overwhelm happens when you unthinkingly attempt to control the experience. But when you can surrender into it, it's a completely different, inexpressibly beautiful experience where you dissolve into an energetic flow where the only points of restriction are the places that need to heal.

5-MeO-DMT has a way of permeating these restricted places, usually resulting in a big release of energy. This can sometimes be intense, as things that are normally locked away and avoided within you are pressed open, but it does get easier with experience. That released energy is the expression of what was needing to heal in the form of words, movement, sounds, or cathartic purging.

Last, there is the mighty breakthrough dose where you take enough to completely dissociate from any sense of yourself, your body, the room you are in, or the planet you are on. For a brief eternity, you are unwound completely, and the energetic release can be massive. Though some people lie still during this experience while everything happens internally, that has never been the case for me.

Most people seem to have little or no memory of the peak of a full breakthrough experience. You'll feel yourself being launched and then fade back into awareness as you start to come down again, and even though your mind doesn't come back with new shiny concepts or ideas to obsess over, things have been deeply moved just the same.

Qualified supervision is absolutely required for a full breakthrough journey because it can be dangerous. People doing it by themselves have died from aspirating vomit, suffocating in a pillow, or drowning in a bathtub. Sometimes under a full breakthrough dose, people will get up and start moving around with no awareness of what they are doing. It's not uncommon at all to thrash wildly on the floor or to vomit. I recommend supervision by a qualified, experienced, and sober guide or sitter when using any amount of this drug.

In my mind, nothing is more powerful for personal growth and healing than a well-timed release on 5-MeO-DMT. When your true intentions for the experience are laser-focused and expressed from that part of you that is trying to heal, nothing can help the process start moving like 5-MeO-DMT can.

But let me be clear, 5-MeO-DMT is not the answer to everything. Rather, it is another tool in your healing toolbox. Usually, a slower exploration and excavation is not only smart but also necessary. You can cause emotional defenses to lock down tighter or even retraumatize yourself by trying to blast your way through your inner world.

The Amusement Park

A disappointing and frustrating trend I've been watching develop is that 5-MeO-DMT experiences are being offered "professionally." These experiences are treated as little more than an amusement park ride because of the short duration of its effect.

Some practitioners playing the role of a *shaman* or *guide* are offering 5-MeO-DMT experiences with no understanding or care for how deeply this medicine can open people up and the vulnerable, emotionally compromised states that they can be left in afterwards.

I know of one person who offers a range of various intensity vape pens for people to experience. He and a helper work with two people at a time in the same room, letting them choose if they want a stronger or weaker next hit to control the experience of the high. The experience of 5-MeO-DMT is being treated as a playground to run around in by people who have no idea what they are doing and who cannot possibly provide the level of support the users might need.

Another person has been offering group 5-MeO-DMT experiences under a religious pretext for many years. There have been numerous complaints from women about inappropriate touching while they were under the influence of the drug. And he's known to keep an electric shock taser on hand in case he accidentally overdoses someone and needs to get them breathing again.

Please have reverence for this incredible medicine. There is no recreational use for it. I can't say that about any other drug on this list. Playing with 5-MeO-DMT carelessly is like shooting a gun into a populated area. Maybe someone won't get hurt, but if not, it was only by luck.

5-MeO-DMT is a mover of deep, deep things, and you could easily find yourself in a terrifying place among people with no training or skill to help you navigate your way back. Always seek qualified support if you desire to explore what this medicine has to offer. We'll talk later in the book about people who offer psychedelic support and what qualifications they should have.

N,N-DMT

The drug N,N-DMT, which is usually just called DMT and sometimes "nn," is known for intense visual hallucinations, even giving the realistic effect of interacting with entities in another dimension. I know people who've done DMT and had profound insights that they felt were of significant value to their lives. I haven't explored this medicine yet, but I do intend to at some point in the future.

DMT only has a place on this list because of its frequent confusion with 5-MeO-DMT. The only thing the two of them have in common are the letters *D*, *M*, and *T* in the name. And because the dosages they require are different, confusing them would be dangerous and possibly even fatal.

Ayahuasca

Ayahuasca, also known as aya, is a drink made with a plant-based N,N-DMT source. Drinking it is different from smoking DMT, both in the overall experience and in how your body processes it.

The drink also contains a naturally occurring MAOI (monoamine oxidase inhibitor) that prevents your body from breaking down the DMT before it can be used. It is usually taken in a group setting, which, when done properly, can move deep emotional energy and provide profound visions and insights. However, many people seem to take these visions as literal when often they are entirely symbolic and meant to be meditated on in the sober light of day.

Ayahuasca offers an incredible opportunity for healing and growth. However, if you are sorting through past traumatic experiences like sexual abuse, rape, PTSD, etc., there is often a lot of fear associated with the feelings that come up. And if you can't find a way to surrender to the flow of those feelings, it can be an overwhelmingly challenging experience. This is what happened for me, and I vowed that I would not go into that medicine space again until I had gone much deeper into my healing process with one-on-one sessions using other psychedelic medicines. In a one-on-one, guided journey any fear that comes up can be managed much more easily and safely, enabling it to flow through and out of you.

Ayahuasca is another drug around which a cottage industry has emerged. You can find facilitators with training and long mentorships who know how to wisely and compassionately handle the massive energies being released in a session.

But you can also find people who've had some big experiences on ayahuasca and decided they wanted to offer the opportunity to others. Most lack intensive training and have not gone through the years of their own deep, properly mentored healing experiences that they need if they are going to have the wisdom to safely run a ceremony. But you'll likely never convince them of this. They go through the motions of being a guide without any true understanding of what that role requires.

There was even a news show about a guy who, upon release from prison, was sent a bottle of ayahuasca by his old cellmate. He went into a shed alone to take it and was deeply moved by the experience. Somehow, from that experience, he deemed himself qualified to offer this "service" to others. Maybe he has way more qualifications than were mentioned in the show, but I didn't see any evidence of it.

Last, there are a growing number of tourist destination opportunities for an ayahuasca experience in Mexico and Central and South America. Some of these essentially offer a Disneyland-style experience, putting up a facade for the tourists, complete with shaman costumes and all of the pomp and circumstance of it, but the medicines are real.

There have been reports of tourists being robbed, raped, or traumatized during their experiences there. Just because these experiences are being offered in or near a rainforest, does not mean they are authentic or being offered by competent experts or honest people.

Likewise, someone indigenous to the region and claiming to come from a long lineage of shamans isn't necessarily the real deal. They could simply be lying, and how would you know? Or that heritage they claim could be based on radical misunderstandings of the medicine journey process and human psychology.

Again, do your homework. A nice-looking website is no indication of quality, only of having enough money to pay for one. None of these places post testimonials by people who didn't have a good experience, so you need to leave their website and do some actual digging to see what you can learn about them and their offerings.

My recommendation is to seek out a competently held experience within your own country, or at least in a first-world country, so you can have access to quality healthcare and support should you need it. Stick to places where there are actual consequences, legal and otherwise, for scamming, lying, or harming people in regard to the ceremonies. These measures tend to help weed out the imposters.

Ketamine

Ketamine, also known as K, Special K, Vitamin K, Lady K, or Ket, is often used as an anesthetic and for pain management, but found its way into recreational use where it's most famous for putting people into the "k-hole," a deeply dissociated state. In more recent years, ketamine has been found to give rapid relief from the symptoms of treatment-resistant depression and suicidal intentions, though some report that its benefits for depression tend to wear off in a few days or weeks.

Ketamine's effects ramp up quickly and the primary effects last only an hour or so with the full effect usually wearing off within a few hours. I utilize ketamine in different ways, always with my intention to aid emotional expansion and exploration.

First, I use it in conjunction with other psychedelic medicines. I find adding ketamine enables me to deeply relax and open for other medicines to work more effectively, but without dampening my emotional experience as would happen with other sedatives. This is the primary way I utilize this medicine. I'll talk more about layering psychedelics together like this later.

Second, I use it by itself as a tool for exploration. I find smaller dosages (less than what would bring about full dissociation) to be a great way to deeply feel into my body where I'm holding any tension. Ketamine makes it easy for your thoughts to run away with you, so I stay present to my breath and scan my body for any tension I might be holding. Massaging or stretching those areas can help with the releasing and relaxing. It's not unusual for memories, emotions, or insights to come bubbling up during this process.

I'd had sinus problems and sinus headaches my whole life. As a teen, my headaches would be so bad, at times I couldn't get out of bed. The headaches became less frequent later in life, but the constant issues of sinus congestion, discomfort, and infections persisted. One evening, as I was working with a moderate dose of ketamine, I learned something profound about myself and my body.

As the drug was settling in, I felt my mind start to run off in different directions, following many streams of thoughts. This is common on ketamine. I let this happen in the background as I started focusing on my breath from deep in my abdomen and started scanning my body for any tension that I might have been holding.

When I came to my head, I could feel a lot of sinus pressure and some pain associated with it. I then noticed that my jaw muscles were tight and that I could follow that tightness down into my neck and even to my shoulders. As I imagined breathing into this area and felt it start to relax, I noticed that this tightness contributed to a felt sense of tension in the roof of my mouth. When that area relaxed, I could instantly feel my sinuses start to clear, and within a few minutes, the felt sense of pressure in them was significantly less.

This was incredible! But I had to be sure of what I'd just discovered. In the following days and weeks, whenever I became aware of having sinus pressure, I would focus on relaxing my jaw, letting my mouth hang open a bit and following the tension into my neck, willing it to relax. From there, I would feel into the tension or pressure around my back teeth and into the roof of my mouth, as if something were pushing the soft palate upwards. Each time I got these areas to relax, I would immediately start feeling my sinuses open also, and any discomfort from them start to diminish.

Layering

Each of the psychedelics I use medicinally is powerful in its own right. But many can also be taken together synergistically, in what I call *layering*, to achieve different experiences.

Sometimes the medicines are taken at the same time, and other times they are staggered during the session. Each variation of layering the psychedelics produces a unique experience. Some combinations can be dangerous or even deadly, so you need to understand any potential drug interactions and verify that what you are taking is what you think you are taking before mixing any kind of drugs.

Two common recreational combinations are LSD and MDMA (known as a candy flip), and MDMA and mushrooms (known as a hippie flip). These particular combinations strongly enhance the desirable aspects of each drug while also making the more challenging effects more manageable. While both LSD and mushrooms can induce anxiety, especially as the drug is first coming on and ramping up, the MDMA all but eliminates that. Combining MDMA with either LSD or mushrooms adds a vibrancy to the experience, especially to the visuals, which are truly something to behold, especially out in nature. There are a multitude of variations possible in layering, depending on the timing of each drug in relation to the other, that can greatly affect the experience. Recreationally, these "flips" are my favorite ways to explore.

In the context of medicine work, MDMA can often be quite "floaty," but mushrooms can ground the experience, so you get the heart-opening safety to explore your inner world but are also able to stay present with it. Further, you get the introspective and insightful nature of the mushrooms without the sometimes edgy or anxious feelings that can come with them.

When these "flips" involve lower doses of either drug, I personally find them only marginally useful in medicine work because I end up feeling really good and want to talk and connect with my guide more than to work. It's like lying in the park with the sun on my face, thinking deep thoughts and chatting with a good friend. Not very productive. But with larger doses of both, I find I move more into ego-dissolution territory where deeper realms within myself start becoming accessible.

As I've grown more experienced in navigating the medicinal psychedelic space, as well as my own inner terrain, I've begun to layer in other psychedelics as a matter of routine. As I stated before, I usually start off most journeys with ketamine at the same time that I'm taking the primary psychedelic (such as MDMA). By the time the peak of the ketamine is wearing off, around forty-five minutes later, the MDMA is really starting to kick in. I can get access to emotional material right away that, without the ketamine, would often take much longer to get into.

On the flip side, using mushrooms with ketamine has enabled me to drop into areas that were normally heavily defended and has triggered significant fear responses that were a challenge to work with. I still do this, knowing not only that the triggering is possible, but also that the whole point of the work is to embrace that fear and allow it to flow so that the wounds behind it heal. But medicine work is never, ever about forcing. Always follow the approach and the medicines that feel like a kindness to yourself in your efforts to help yourself.

I will also commonly layer 5-MeO-DMT into sessions with other medicines. Often I use it on the comedown to help keep releasing the energy that started moving during the session. This isn't a matter of forcing something; instead, when something is asking to release but can't, I find that layering 5-MeO-DMT into the experience is often a way to get it moving.

Using 5-MeO-DMT in this way is not for the fainthearted, nor is it for those new to medicine work. Layered with other psychedelics, 5-MeO-DMT is guaranteed to be incredibly intense, and you'll almost certainly be feeling the emotional effects of the combination for days or even weeks to follow. Those effects are a positive aspect of the work, but they can also be quite challenging.

Future Exploration

There are a few medicines that are well known to be potent tools for healing that I have not explored yet, but plan to. Iboga/ibogaine and peyote (mescaline) are at the top of my list. I am interested in seeing what these have to offer, but need to find guides and settings for them that feel right to me. I'd also like to further explore ayahuasca once I find the right facilitator.

CHAPTER 4

HOW I GOT HERE

As a kid, I was sensitive, intelligent, and highly perceptive. I was also often hyper, loud, impulsive, and never sure why I'd done the things that I did. Had I been born a few decades later, I'm sure I would have been pumped full of a wide array of drugs to "fix" me.

I was raised by a single mother who, being profoundly wounded herself, was most often emotionally disengaged and disinterested, unless she found herself overwhelmed, when she would lash out in intense anger. I still have flashbacks of seeing the look on her face I perceived as pure hatred, as she stood screaming at me for one thing or another. It wasn't usually a matter of physical abuse, outside of some pretty intense spankings with a belt. Instead, the abuse was primarily verbal, psychological, and emotional.

There were nice times too. I remember when I was young and had fallen asleep one morning on the sofa watching Saturday morning cartoons. The next thing I knew, I was being awakened by several tiny pink puppies licking my face. Our dog had given birth to them recently and my mother had placed them on my chest as a surprise. I can still distinctly remember what their puppy breath smelled like.

There were other positive moments, but I have to struggle hard to bring them to mind. What I mostly remember of my childhood is an emotional void, interrupted only by criticism or the intensity of the screaming. In a home without any semblance of personal boundaries, I instinctively learned to not let **me**, my heart, ever be accessible or seen, so that my sense of self couldn't be overwhelmed, which felt like death.

Strangely, it was also a life in which sentimentality often substituted for real human connection or love. Birthdays and Christmas were always times for huge piles of presents. Gifts were a big show of sentimental love, but they could be weaponized also.

When I was in the fifth grade, my mom came home one evening with a big ice cream sundae complete with crunchy chopped nuts, a huge pile of whipped cream, and a maraschino cherry on top. I remember being so delighted because that kind of thing so rarely happened. Then, when my happiness must have seemed that it had peaked, my mom asked me a question: *What happened to that money in my bathroom cabinet?*

She worked side jobs to help pay the bills and was often paid in cash for them. I had been sneaking a few dollars here and there to buy candy or soda with my friends at the local convenience store. I didn't have any money of my own and didn't think that she would have noticed it missing. Clearly, she had a right to confront me about it and have a talk about not taking what wasn't mine.

Instead, she wanted me to feel really good before she confronted me, to ensure that any shame I felt for the theft would be maximized. I sat there with a bite of ice cream melting in my mouth and could neither swallow nor spit it out — it having gone from delicious to a bitter chemical taste. My solar plexus truly, deeply burned with a sense of shame and humiliation. I felt pure agony, knowing that she'd done this to me on purpose. She used my feeling loved from receiving a special treat to open me up, so that the blade could sink in deep, and the punishment was maximized. Maximizing punishment like this was a common theme in my extended family. An easy example was a horse that my grandfather had ridden for over twenty years. One day as he was riding, it became spooked and threw him off, breaking his neck and leaving him crippled — so one of my uncles shot it in the head, killing it in retaliation.

Often, if I truly loved or enjoyed something, it became a bad thing, and it had to be taken away. So favorite toys or hobbies or interests were found to somehow be wrong, evidence that I was "living in a fantasy world," and I needed to be deprived of them to show me what "real" life was. Or I needed to be punished by being grounded from them for so long that by the time I got them back, I'd outgrown them. I learned that showing too much joy or love for anything would bring punishment.

I was always cautious, even within myself, to never allow myself to fully feel joy or enjoyment about anything for fear that whatever it was would somehow be taken away. I had a real sense in the back of my mind that God or "life" would take notice if I enjoyed or appreciated something, and that I would be punished for it. I didn't so much think these things in words as they were woven into the fabric of my reality, like gravity or needing air to breathe. It wasn't anything I thought to question because it was just how life seemed to work.

Decades later, through psychedelic healing work, I learned not only that these beliefs could be questioned, but also that the act of truly, honestly doing so would cause them to start unwinding and dissolving all on their own. A couple of years into the medicine work, I realized I didn't feel that way much at all anymore. As I write this, I know that there are some deep remnants of that fear within me that still exert some influence. But subjectively, it feels like a tiny fraction of what it previously was, and I feel confident that this, too, will release when it is ready.

Accumulating Developmental Trauma: The Development of Complex PTSD

My grandparents had taken me in as an infant, and my earliest bonds were with them, as my mom was young, immature, and focused on finding the life she'd wanted before getting knocked up had taken her future away from her.

As an infant and toddler, I spent more time with them than with my mother. When my mom decided to move us half an hour away to her own place, that life was upended. My grandparents were far from perfect at parenting, but as a cute baby I'd received love and attention, the best they could give.

I've been told stories and have watched old home movies showing how my grandpa and I were inseparable when I was young, and of how much I loved him. When he'd try to leave to go about his farmwork, I'd sit on his boot, wrapping my arms and legs around his leg, so he'd have to drag his foot with me on it, giggling away as he worked his way towards the door. Often, at these times, he'd scoop me up and take me with him in his pickup as he went out to check on his cattle or crops in the various plots of land he owned.

When I was young, I did feel love for and from my grandparents, though it was often conditional, with shame being used to control my behavior. They were deeply wounded people who wounded their own children, including my mother, who passed that wounding on to me. I'm sure they came from a long line of wounded people. That's how it works until someone becomes self-aware enough to break the cycle. Breaking that cycle in my lineage started, imperfectly, with me.

When I was in the second or third grade, a teacher was concerned about me and called my mom in for a conference. They decided that the teacher's concerns were the result of my not having a father at home — I guess the screaming didn't come up. The teacher said that he and his wife would be willing to take me out to do fun things like attending local football games. I never cared for football, but I did like popcorn, hot dogs, and soda, so it was fun attending games with them for the short time it lasted. I can remember feeling curious about what he saw that made him so concerned about me — I had no idea. I was just being me so far as I could tell, but I also knew in my heart that there must be a lot that was wrong about me.

In the fourth and fifth grade, I was bullied mercilessly. It was a long walk to school, and a group of boys found great sport in chasing me to school and back home again, trying to corner me and get me to fight them. It went on for months, and I spent every day feeling terrified that they were going to catch me, helpless to stop it, and hopeless that it would ever end or that anyone would help. I never felt safe. I stopped going outside to play and spent most of my time hiding at home watching TV.

I remember asking my mom for help, and her response was to angrily scream at me that I needed to grow some balls and face the bullies. She only became concerned sometime later when I told her with complete sincerity that I would be taking a knife with me to school and that I was going to kill the next motherfucker that attacked me. I guess that this was too much "balls" for her, and I was immediately transferred to a new school and thankfully never faced bullying like that again.

At one point in junior high school, I came into possession of three kittens. I can't remember how I got them, but they were a ray of sunshine in an endlessly bleak landscape. We were living with my mother's boyfriend in a house on a large lot in a rural area of Oklahoma, and it was a cold, icy winter. The kittens lived in the garage with a heater, and I spent a lot of my free time with them every day. I cared for them and took in the warmth of these little creatures needing my care. I'd snuggle with them as I watched TV or played with them, letting them wrestle with my hands. I felt a connection to something else alive, and for a while they gave me some of what I'd been so desperately missing.

Then one day my mother's boyfriend started up his truck in the driveway to the sound of a loud series of thumps from under the hood. The kittens had crawled up by the engine for warmth and were caught up in the radiator fan and belts when the engine was started. I learned about it when my mother came into the house and angrily gave me a shovel. She said that Jim wanted me to go clean up the mess on the ice outside because my cats had gotten into his truck, and he didn't want to have to deal with it.

For my mom, me causing a problem of any kind for her boyfriend was the absolute worst thing I could do. In those moments, I was perceived as a direct threat to her relationship. She had no thought or concern that the only living things I felt any emotional connection to had just been torn to shreds in a horrific spray of blood on the driveway ice. She didn't care what it did to me to go outside and see how one of them hadn't been killed right away and had pulled itself across the ice in a smeared streak of red.

What I felt was of no concern as the shovel was pushed into my hands with a fearful hatred, which was a reconfirmation that if I allowed myself to feel for something, to love something, that it would be taken from me in an angry and violent fashion.

High School

I'd been looking forward to being able to drive for a long time, and at fifteen, I finally got my driver's permit. I was so happy and excited to be able to drive and soon would have my real license and be able to venture out on my own. With a permit, I had to have a licensed driver with me to practice driving, so for my first excursion I was going to drive my mom into town to do some shopping.

I was excited and nervous as I backed us out of the driveway. I turned to put my hand on the back of the passenger seat to look over my shoulder and see behind me. My mom, for some reason, needed to look behind us too and turned her head at the same time, causing me to accidentally bump her face with my elbow. It wasn't that hard, but it shocked us both. But when she angrily screamed at me — *You goddamned motherfucker, now people are going to think that Jim hits me!* — something inside of me gave way. I felt so small, without any value, and so alone that the intense wave of prickly shame caused a vital part of me to finally collapse in on itself.

I barely made it through high school, as my ability to focus on schoolwork or have any real consideration for the future was almost nonexistent. What today would likely be labeled as ADHD, or with a competent therapist would have been recognized as symptomatic of Complex PTSD, was just seen as me being lazy and undisciplined. I had no idea why I couldn't do better in school — I just couldn't. Year after year, in parent-teacher conferences with my mother, I'd hear the various teachers say some version of, *He's very smart, but he just won't apply himself.* Then they'd both sit there and shake their heads in agreement that they just didn't understand it, and it was such a pity.

When I discovered alcohol, it was like the friend that I was missing. Drinking became a form of self-medication to help me manage the pain of my despair. Through much of my junior and senior years in high school I would frequently drink in the evenings and often even at lunchtime during school. I have no idea how the teachers never smelled it on me or noticed that I couldn't walk a straight line, but somehow this became a frequent part of my high school routine.

When I was sixteen, my grandfather became sick and was admitted to the hospital, and before I could go see him, he'd passed away. I wanted to have spoken to him and to have held his hand one last time. Throughout the entire process of the family grieving for his loss and at his funeral, I was only able to cry once for less than thirty seconds before my body clamped down on feeling anything at all. My unexpressed grief in high school led to me further shutting down and disengaging almost completely. It wasn't until more than thirty years later, as I was coming down from MDMA in a medicine work journey, that I burst into deep, wracking sobs expressing the pain, loneliness, and loss that I'd felt when my grandpa had died.

Near the end of high school, I was spending a lot of time with a cousin my same age, our friend Kevin, and two girls who were usually in our group. We often had fun, drank and laughed together. Those were some of the best times I remember from back then. Then one day, as we hung out at one of their houses, it turned out that Kevin had been upset by something or another that I'd said, and we were going to have to fight in the backyard. Red-headed and freckled, Kevin was a lot bigger than me, and I was really scared.

I remember my cousin holding a revolver as he stood by the back door into the house. I know that he wouldn't have actually shot me, but I was shocked that he was standing there holding it to send the message that I wasn't getting out of this. The two girls were laughing and enjoying themselves, seemingly eager to enjoy the show at my expense.

I froze, dumbfounded. I felt myself making fists, but I couldn't will myself to fight. My only group of friends had turned on me for reasons I didn't understand. I was sure I'd said or done something stupid that needed to be worked out with Kevin. But instead of any attempt to resolve it, I felt like I was being tossed aside like garbage, as if I'd never mattered to any of them at all.

I could only stand there as Kevin punched me in the face over and over again, shredding the inside of my lips and cheeks against my teeth. Finally, when all the fun had been wrung from the moment, the group grew tired and left me there shocked and disbelieving at how everything that had felt good to me just a little while before was now gone.

At the time, I was staying with my mother's ex-boyfriend after they had broken up. When I got home, I went to his bedroom, sat on his bed, and took his polished 9mm semiautomatic pistol out of the nightstand. I sat staring at it, feeling its cool touch and surprising weight in my hand. Then I put it to my head, pressing it firmly to my temple.

With most semiautomatic pistols, there is a range of slack in the trigger, a distance that the trigger can move freely before you feel the resistance of the point at which you are actually engaging the trigger mechanism. With my finger on the trigger, I played with the slack in it, pulling it right up to the edge of where it would go off and daring myself to pull just a little more.

As I sat on the bed crying, I wanted the endless loneliness and despair to end. Had I pulled that trigger even a millimeter farther, the gun would have gone off and my life would have ended that day. It was one simple thing that floated into my awareness that stopped the forward momentum of the suicide in its tracks. I found that I was curious about what would happen next in the unfolding story of my life, that some underlying hope for something more still existed. Still sobbing, I put the gun away, and serious thoughts of suicide didn't cross my mind again for quite some time.

From high school, I joined the Navy under a misguided notion that I could become a Navy SEAL. That fantasy continued until I realized that regular Navy boot camp physical training was kicking my ass, and SEAL training would be a thousand times more difficult. After that humbling realization, I settled into the idea that I'd get by with my mind, not my brawn or bravery. Mostly though, my buddies and I hung out, chased girls, and drank to excess.

Perpetuating Relational Wounding

After the Navy, I moved back to Sacramento to live with a young woman I'd been seeing. She was a sweet, kind person, a gymnast going to college to become a physical therapist. It was my first serious relationship.

There I began working in an engineering firm as their in-house IT guy. I loved the challenge, the responsibility, and the constant process of learning, progressing, and improving. But while my budding professional career was taking off and I felt great about it, my romantic relationship was strained and steadily falling apart.

She offered real love, connection, and an opportunity for me to truly be seen. But I was completely unprepared for such care and unable to receive it. Her emotional availability unconsciously triggered too much pain and fear in me, and I found myself frequently angry, jealous, suspicious, and overwhelmed. Sometimes I ended up screaming, much like my mother had screamed at me. I'd grown up without having my own boundaries recognized and honored, so I had no capacity to recognize or honor hers. It was actually a relief when she finally ended things.

Taking a Trip Without Leaving the Farm

Soon after the breakup, I had my first experience of psychedelics. Stan was an interesting guy who had both his bachelor's and master's degrees from Ivy League schools while barely in his early twenties. Smart — really, really smart. He also loved the Grateful Dead, Phish, and other jam bands that constantly toured. At some point, he asked if I'd like to try acid, and without even knowing what it was, I emphatically said yes. If this guy thought acid was worth doing, I wanted to check it out.

We met at my apartment, where Stan gave us both a tiny square of paper and told me to put it under my tongue. We left to go on a walk, and I found myself playing with the paper with my tongue, chewing on it, and eventually, in an absent-minded moment, swallowing it. Luckily it had been there long enough for me to absorb the whole dose.

As the drug started to set in, I felt a new low-level sense of energy humming in the background. Walking felt a little strange, like I had somehow lost the knack for doing it right, and my movements felt awkward. My visual field was altered, things looked "trippy," colors more intense. There was a warping distortion in anything I'd stare at. I found all of that interesting, but the most incredible part was what was happening to my mind, which felt activated and engaged on a level I'd never known before.

As we walked around my neighborhood, Stan kept engaging me in interesting conversation, offering all sorts of cool, mind-bending thought experiments. Once, he asked me if I'd ever experienced déjà vu. *Sure*, I replied. Then he asked, *So, how do you know the difference between remembering something that you've experienced before and only having the feeling of remembering it?* On and on we went with a conversation that to this day remains one of my favorites of all time.

The next day as I got ready for work, I understood clearly that I would be categorizing my life as before I tried LSD and after. I knew for certain that I wanted to see what else was possible with this kind of inner exploration. Nothing had ever felt more right to me before.

When trying to explain the experience to another friend, I used an image of my everyday mind as a large warehouse with a single light bulb coming down from the center of the ceiling to just above the floor. It only lit a small area and the rest was completely dark. During the trip, though, it seemed like many more lights were turned on, giving me access to much more of what my mind was capable of. After the trip, the lighting wasn't anywhere near as bright as it had been during the trip, but the bulb I was left with felt considerably brighter. I was changed in a profound way.

Insights and Setbacks

I've always appreciated the saying *Wisdom is what you get just after you needed it.* It wasn't too long after that first psychedelic experience that an insight came bubbling up into my awareness that all of the issues in my former romantic relationship were because of me.

I saw clearly how horribly I'd treated my girlfriend out of my own feelings of overwhelm that had nothing to do with her, and I felt genuine, righteous shame about it. This new self-awareness and self-honesty was incredibly basic, only showing the broadest strokes of what was going on, but it was a start. It was progress, and it stoked the flame of my curiosity and desire for more.

I eventually moved on to a new job with more opportunities and responsibilities and I started dating someone new. When I was approved to transfer to a new position down in San Diego within this same company, she bravely packed up and moved with me.

We were together a couple of years when it was starting to feel to both of us that things had about run their course. But then she got pregnant and we felt a renewed sentimentality and decided to get married, buy a house, and build a family together. During this time I also left my job to start my own computer security consulting company.

Having a family was overwhelming for me for reasons that I couldn't fully understand. I mostly immersed myself in long hours of work each day to avoid feeling overwhelmed at home.

I loved my daughter and, out of a misguided notion of how life works, I instinctively kept that love stuffed away deep inside for fear of what might happen if I didn't. We hung on to that marriage for a couple of years before my wife decided it was time to move on.

As a part-time single dad, I wasn't engaging with my two-year-old daughter much. I moved easily into a state of feeling overwhelmed when watching her by myself and would disengage. I was vaguely aware of what was happening and initially determined that she was better off spending more time with her mother than with me. At the time, this was likely true because I had no ability at all to affect any change in my state of mind. Everything that I would otherwise have had to give to her was locked away deep inside, behind feelings of fear and shame.

It was on a mushroom trip that I experienced a flash of insight that illuminated my true desire to be a part of her life, and that I had to find a way to dig deeper and try harder. My ex was surprised when I called and asked for a 50:50 split in our parenting time, but she agreed and seemed happy at my newfound commitment.

I soon started dating someone new and our relationship proved highly charged with reactivity and drama. During this time, as my everyday state of anxiety and feelings of overwhelm steadily grew, my ability to parent slipped further and further away. I was often emotionally withdrawn and at times, feeling overwhelmed, I snapped under the pressure and yelled at my daughter or in her presence. I further developed a quick trigger and an aggressive temper that came out in my parenting, relationships, and my work.

I tried to be what I could figure out a good dad should be, but the crushing anxiety I lived within every day was firmly in the driver's seat. My overwhelming feelings defined my reality completely. My body would go into a depressive state to shut down the overwhelm, which would then leave me feeling lethargic and unmotivated. I would consume cup after cup of coffee in search of some energy to function, which only amplified my anxiety, making me even more volatile. I couldn't see any of what was happening clearly, I couldn't even recognize that it was anxiety and fear that was driving all of it. Day by day, life only felt more terrible, overwhelming and like it was too much to endure.

Suicide ideation became my default escape mechanism when I started feeling too overwhelmed, and I used it a lot. I thought of death as my backup plan in case life became too out of control and overwhelming. I could always take control that way.

I started sedating myself increasingly with Xanax, Valium, and/or alcohol in the evenings to try to have some control, but I also began recognizing how desperately out of control I actually was.

Therapy and Developing Self-Awareness

I sought out a therapist to help me with my anger, to sort out what was happening in this relationship, and most importantly, how to do better for my daughter. It was with the most incredible good fortune, an act of grace, that I found a truly gifted one.

Just as my first psychedelic trip was my first big pivot point towards self-awareness and healing my wounded psyche, meeting my therapist Taffy was the second. Working with her changed the arc of my life as she gave me hope for more than just surviving it, teaching me how to become more self-aware and self-actualized, which empowered me to drive my own growth forward. This is why I dedicated my first book, *Present Moment Awareness*, to her and also to my daughter, who was at the heart of my push to be and do better.

In my many sessions with Taffy, sometimes as many as two a week and up to two hours at a time, we engaged in talk therapy to help bring my story out into the room so we could look at it and begin to understand how it had affected me and brought me to this point.

We also worked on developing my self-awareness. Through a technique she used known as Hakomi Mindful Somatic Psychotherapy, I learned how to perceive and feel into my emotions, giving whatever came up a shape, color, texture, temperature, weight, and whatever else wanted to be expressed about it. This put me in the place of an observer, like a scientist watching through a microscope, rather than having those same emotions completely define my sense of self and reality.

As I learned to calmly observe each layer of emotion, I was amazed to see that instead of becoming more intense, the feelings would just flow through me. Then, whatever was underneath that emotion would present itself, and we'd go through the process again, layer after layer. Anger would release to reveal fear, which would release to reveal loneliness. This, in turn, when released, revealed a deep ocean of sadness. Again, and again, we ventured inward, developing skills that I continue to use to this day.

Outside of the therapies and tools that Taffy employed, her incredible effectiveness as a therapist stemmed from the fact that she'd done a huge amount of her own deep healing work. It never felt like she was talking based on concepts that had sounded good when picked up from a book or seminar. What she said seemed to come from an authentic place of true understanding, empathy, and compassion. I was only able to go deep into myself with her because she was holding a space that energetically was as deep, and deeper.

During my work with Taffy, I became heavily invested in learning as much as I could about psychology and spirituality, voraciously reading everything Taffy recommended and anything else that stood out as possibly being helpful.

It was then that I started developing a sense of discernment and a healthy skepticism for all concepts and belief systems. I was driven to find a way to actually change, to truly grow and not simply get lost in some trendy new concept or another. I'd strip anything I felt was worth considering down to its simplest form, and then see how it resonated not in my mind as some idealized notion, but in my body at the level of understanding and wisdom.

Using Psychedelics with Purpose

It was also in this time that I started exploring psychedelics with more purpose and more frequency. I would often take mushrooms or LSD and take long walks by myself to see what insights might prove useful.

Each time the drugs started settling in on my walk, I had an image in my mind of a warrior, sword drawn, jumping into a wide black hole in the ground. I didn't know what I was going to find or how things were going to go, but I had the strong intention that I was going to undo the "bad" in me to be able to let more of the good out.

As we'll cover later, this isn't the best way to look at it. You don't get rid of the things you don't like in yourself, but rather you embrace them and help them to heal. It's all **you** in there. But at the time, the warrior approach was the understanding that I had, and in its own way, it gave me the drive to keep going inward to learn and grow.

Here is where both my understanding of myself, and my ability to be self-aware in the moment, began improving dramatically. The challenges and pain brought up in my current romantic relationship had kept the door open for deeply introspective work in therapy and with psychedelics. The insights and shifts in perspective kept landing as my hunger to know, do, and be something more than what my childhood had made me kept growing.

While vacationing on Maui, I met a really cool couple who introduced me to MDMA. My first experience was on a warm Hawaiian evening spent in that beautiful space, talking, sharing, and being in a simple, but real, connection with them.

It was my first-ever experience, outside of therapy, of a co-regulated emotional exchange with others, a connection, as opposed to always waiting to see how someone else was going to feel, what that would make them do, and how that was going to then make me feel. That experience woke me up to a whole new possibility of human existence, of being in connection with others.

After that, I found a therapist that was willing to let me take MDMA and come to their office to talk things out with them. It was my first-ever attempt to take psychedelic use to a deeper level. We did this a few times, and it was indeed beneficial. But the professional office setting, the shorter duration of only two hours, and my need to navigate myself home afterwards, limited how effective it could be.

Look at Me Now, Ma, I'm a Writer!

It was at this time during the late nineties that I sold some technology and a methodology I had developed for assessing computer security to a large company, closed the business, and retired at age twenty-nine.

Eckhart Tolle's book *The Power of Now* was all the rage, and while I liked the book a lot, my pragmatic mind wanted to boil the essence of what I was gleaning down into a practical way to apply it in everyday life. It was then that the idea for the Focus Tool was born.

Back before smartphones that can run applications, we only had pagers and cell phones with physical buttons. Wanting a way to keep practicing bringing myself back into the moment, I developed a small battery-powered device that would alert me randomly throughout the day. At intervals, somewhere between twenty minutes and two hours apart, the alert would sound, signaling me to snap out of whatever I was focusing on and bring myself back into the moment to check in on what was happening for me mentally and emotionally as well as what was happening around me. It worked great, and while the device was going into production to make it available for sale, the instruction manual for it kept growing. Eventually it became my first book, *Present Moment Awareness*.

Initially, the book was self-published and did pretty well on Amazon, which caught the eye of Eckhart Tolle's publisher. They offered to take over the publishing of it and I readily agreed.

Before this, I didn't have a sense of scale as to how much more growth was needed or even possible for me. But once I was a published author, the new status went to my head more than a little, and the blinders were firmly in place for a long time. Along with now having some money in the bank after having sold my business, being a published author was the kind of validation that my deep insecurities had always yearned for. These were things I could hold up to the world to seemingly prove I had worth, and I leaned into it heavily.

It is to my close friends' great credit that they kept a sense of humor about this and stuck by me, because in my arrogance, I must have been a challenge to be around at times.

Diving Headfirst to Rock Bottom

When I was in my early thirties, Taffy let me know she'd be moving away from the San Diego area and could refer me to a new therapist should I wish it. In addition, my previous chaotic relationship ended, and another replaced it.

I tried working with another therapist, but it was never the same. I couldn't build the same kind of trust. So I drifted away from therapeutic work and eventually from psychedelics as well, with the exception of very occasional recreational uses with friends.

Even though I had made amazing inroads in self-awareness and personal growth, I still had emotional wounds at the core of my being that continued to exert considerable control over my experience of life.

In my mid-thirties, I found myself starting to cycle in and out of depressive periods more frequently. Repeatedly diagnosed as having depression, I tried a wide range of antidepressants, none of which helped. Many only made things feel much worse.

I stopped working or supporting my book completely, and my bank account dwindled over time as I couldn't bring myself to do anything to help myself. I lost my home, went through bankruptcy, and basically hit rock bottom and had to start all over again.

I tried dating for a while, but nothing serious developed, and then I went more than a decade without even trying to date. The deep, deep insecurities about my worth and desirability expanded over time to take over any other thoughts of myself. I didn't just worry that nobody would find me attractive or want to be with me, I felt it as a certainty.

At one point in my early forties, I had a party at my home with lots of booze flowing and a fair amount of cocaine getting passed around. I've only tried cocaine a few times and am not really a fan, but it seemed fun that night as we all talked enthusiastically at high speed about important life issues.

That night, I ended up making out with a female friend whom I had felt attracted to for quite a while. While it was happening, I felt a huge swell in my chest that maybe I was desirable, want-able, and worthy. It was a ray of light in the darkness that I hadn't felt in a long time.

We eventually fell asleep before things could go too far, and the next morning she seemed uncomfortable and embarrassed, which I took deeply, deeply to heart. The meaning my mind gave to it was that she was ashamed for having shared some intimacy with me because she saw me as so far beneath her. I spiraled down into myself for weeks, steadily shutting down a little more each day. It was what felt like an undeniable validation of every bad thing I had ever felt and believed about myself, and I just couldn't find it in me to keep fighting with it anymore.

I'd drink a couple bottles of wine or half a bottle of scotch each night and listen to sad or melancholy music to help me work up to committing suicide. It took several days of this before I could actually bring myself to try. With a large amount of alcohol in my system, I took a fistful of muscle relaxers, sleeping pills, and painkillers that I had around the house, and I went to bed with the intention that I was not going to wake up again. In that moment, that was just fine with me.

I groggily became aware of myself some time later, and some part of my mind thought that since I wasn't dead, I should probably try to live. I got up to stand but my legs wouldn't work, so I pulled myself across the floor with my arms, like a soldier crawling under barbed wire, to get myself to the bathroom and make myself throw up. Once I'd purged, I passed out again on the bathroom floor for almost ten hours.

Something in me changed after that. I was emotionally numb and had completely closed out any possibility for romantic connection, as well as pulling back from most of my friends. I got into the groove of building up a business again and focused on work that included a lot of travel to keep me distracted. I rarely did anything psychedelic but I definitely drank too much and frequently took Xanax to knock me out so I could sleep. This went on for a couple of years until, on a good day, a conversation with a friend led me to trying a guided psychedelic journey.

I Found a Toad on the Path to Salvation

For years I'd heard about "DMT" as this incredible psychedelic with unbelievable visual hallucinations. If you took a big enough dose, you could even leave your body with your consciousness intact and arrive in a completely different reality. **You** would still be there, but your body would be gone, and you would be traveling through fantastical landscapes and meeting entities. Sign me up!

I had wanted to try it for a long time but never had the opportunity until a friend of mine mentioned knowing someone who hosted journeys for DMT. I was put in contact with the right people and paid the deposit to be a part of the group.

There were six of us participating, plus the guide and his two assistants, who took turns helping him work with each person. We met in the morning for introductions, heard a talk about the experience, and practiced the long inhale on the pipe required to get a full breakthrough.

The guide was impressive; I'd never met anyone like him. We spoke about our intentions for what we wanted from the experience, and then we waited on the beautiful grounds of the property in silence as we each took our turn to work with the guide and an assistant for our individual journeys.

When it was my turn, I was surprised at how truly terrified I felt, my heart hammering in my chest. This was new to me — I had never felt any fear about doing psychedelics before.

The large room where the ceremony took place was dark and comfortable. There was a large, soft mat in the middle of the floor, and a pillow for my head. The smell of sage was strong, and the ambient music was powerful, as if ushering in an event too big to even conceive of.

I sat on the floor with the assistant's back to mine, giving me something to lean against. The guide sat in front of me holding a long, thin, glass pipe with a bulb on the end containing what looked like fine tan flakes. I was frightened, but I didn't know of what. I felt like I might throw up or panic and run out of the room.

I told the guide I was scared, and he smiled gently, put a hand on my chest, and encouraged me to take deep breaths for as long as I needed, and to nod when I was ready. After a few moments, I got a grip on myself and nodded. He held the pipe to my lips as he gently heated the end with a torch lighter and encouraged me to inhale slowly.

I watched the stuff in the end of the pipe seem to melt and then let off a thick white vapor that I was breathing in. With toad, it takes about a thirty-second inhale to get enough for a full breakthrough. But part way through, I thought that I might cough, so I had to pause and swallow a few times while still holding my breath. Then I finished the inhale and was gently laid back onto the pillow.

Almost instantly I came to a jarring realization: the drug I was doing was not what I'd originally thought it was. I'd mistakenly expected the highly visual N,N-DMT. But I'd learn later that this was 5-MeO-DMT, and they are nothing alike.

Instead of being thrust into a visual psychedelic experience, I had the distinct feeling of intense acceleration. I felt like I was coming apart into individual atoms and then into something even less than that. I experienced a burst of terror as I could clearly feel the normal restraints on my emotions opening up and then... I was gone.

The next thing I knew, I was lying on my side and sobbing with an intensity I'd never known before. I could hear myself saying, *I'm so alone*, over and over and over again. The guide's assistant lay down behind me and held me close as I let out a lifetime of pent-up sadness I'd long since forgotten I could even feel. I was tapped into an ocean of despair at living a life so emotionally separated from any other human being, and the release of that energy felt amazing. The gratitude I feel for it even years later can still make me tear up. As I was resting afterwards, and the experience was settling in, I realized a few incredible things.

First, I was no longer an atheist. I had let go of rebelling against my family's hypocritical Christian doctrine and was left with a sense of connection to *all-that-is*. This brought a quieting, a settling, that even years later has never left me for a moment.

I hadn't found any kind of god, nor did I find an attraction to any religion. But what I did find was an undeniable, felt connection to whatever *all-that-is*, is. I'd had a direct experience of being egoless, and from that perspective the interwoven fabric of reality, the one thing, stood out as beyond obvious. From that place, it seemed impossible to have ever seen it in any other way.

And, of course, as I came down from the high, I could feel myself being woven back together, including most, but not all, of the beliefs that limit my vision and hide the obvious truth from my everyday experience of life. But I also brought back a felt connection to a greater truth, a simple truth, that required no beliefs, rules, judgments, or concepts on my part. The felt understanding of being a part of that infinite tapestry, while also being all of it, is all that I personally require of spirituality.

Second, I found that for the first time I could remember, I had real hope. I knew without a doubt that I could heal the wounds I'd always suffered from and find my way to a new experience of life.

I'd done a variety of psychedelics in my life, but never like this. The difference wasn't just in the drug itself, it was also in the power of having the experience under the capable protection of a truly amazing guide. He created a space energetically so vast, so deep, with none of his own emotional baggage in the way, so that I could open into that space as deeply as was possible.

Doing this same drug by myself or with someone who wasn't as experienced, talented, and professional would absolutely not have yielded the same results. I've since tried doing 5-MeO-DMT sessions with other guides who were disappointingly unqualified, and the experience was a pale imitation of the real thing.

The next morning the group came together to discuss our experiences. For some, it was a deep release; for others, it was more superficial: clarity on relationship issues, decisions coming together around big life changes, and so on. And it was clear that when the participants had truly asked for a deep healing, they got it. But when they asked for something less, they got that too. It was my first lesson on the importance of setting honest and clear intentions when working with psychedelics. *Go for the roots, not the leaves.*

As we were all saying our goodbyes, I heard the guide in the next room sharing that he was offering a limited number of one-on-one medicine sessions, and if anyone thought they might be interested to please let him know. I can't remember, but I must have been knocking people aside to get to him as fast as my feet would take me. I knew with absolute certainty that this was what I needed. Something deep within me had been awakened, it was calling out to heal, and I fully intended to do my best to make it happen. We exchanged information, and my saga of healing trauma with psychedelic medicines had officially begun.

CHAPTER 5

HEALING AND BECOMING WHOLE

Unexpressed emotions will never die.
They are buried alive and will come forth later in uglier ways.

— SIGMUND FREUD

My first psychedelic guide once told me something that changed my whole perspective on working with psychedelics and emotional healing. He said, *If you cut your arm, your body knows how to heal it. Your body knows how to heal you emotionally too, if you'll let it.*

Once I became a bit self-aware and had some sense of the limited and dysfunctional ways I operated in my life, my response was usually to see myself as damaged or broken. A lot of people seem to think of themselves in these terms, especially people with trauma and related defensive mechanisms that cause them distress or problems in their lives.

But terms like "damaged" and "broken" suggest something permanent that has to be worked around for the rest of your life. Thinking of yourself or others in this way leaves little or no room for the possibility of healing or growth. What we are is *wounded*, and wounds can heal. When you can feel the truth of this in your body, the shift in perspective changes everything.

57

Emotional wounds are made when the feelings generated during an experience are so overwhelming that the psyche labels them as a threat, too dangerous to be felt. The psyche builds defenses to protect those wounds from being triggered and those feelings coming up again. Anger was always one of my defenses. When a wounded place was triggered, anger was my automatic defense to push back on who or whatever was perceived to be triggering me, to create some space. But from this early, limited perspective, I could only believe that something or someone had made me angry and my anger was justified. I couldn't see that I was triggered *because I had a trigger*, a defense mechanism for an emotional wound, in the first place.

It's not just intensely traumatic events that create triggers, though those triggers tend to be the most profound. Many experiences that invoke a strong sense of fear, shame, frustration or grief can lead the psyche to lock down that moment and its corresponding emotional energy as a means of protecting against that particular tone or resonance of feeling being experienced again. The psyche may do this in response to a single overwhelming experience or to multiple traumas that build up over time.

Healing happens when we navigate through the defenses and into these wounded places. Here you allow those emotional wounds to fully express themselves as many times as is required to enable the natural process of emotional expression to fully come to completion.

If you have a broken finger, it's natural that you would be on guard to prevent something from bumping it because you instinctively understand a bump would hurt a lot. But that instinct to defend against the pain and further injury recedes once the wounded finger has healed and no longer hurts when touched. In the same way, once emotional wounds are healed, there isn't a need for defenses and coping strategies to keep life experiences from touching them because they are no longer painful to touch.

Those defenses that can control your life, whether you are consciously aware of them or not, naturally start to recede when your psyche perceives that they are no longer needed. The life energy previously used to constantly monitor for threats comes back into the whole of you, to be used in new and positive ways. As the felt sense of vulnerability naturally diminishes, the triggers protecting those vulnerable points get less and less sensitive over time. This type of healing is what psychedelic medicine work is all about.

Sure, there are scars when wounds heal, but scars don't hurt when touched. Those scars are the wisdom and understanding that come from past experience. Unhealed wounds leave you in a perpetual state of perceived vulnerability. Scars give you the confidence to navigate life with a level of wisdom, discernment, compassion, and empathy that someone without those particular scars can never have.

Relating to Your Inner World

Some will discuss psychedelic medicine experiences from an anthropomorphic perspective, where it's the medicine that chooses where to go and how deep. And others talk more spiritually, about spirit, God, or other external forces guiding the healing. I don't find this helpful, as it takes the responsibility for my healing out of my own hands. I try to avoid language and concepts that give agency over the process to anything or anyone other than myself, because it's my choice and my intention that allows it to happen.

I find it helpful to relate to those wounded, defended places as younger aspects of me that were fractured off and locked away inside a prison of fear or shame. I can feel the older, wiser "me," along with my guide, holding a witnessing space for them, giving comfort, love, and support. I do my best to allow those aspects of myself to express their feelings and to feel safe, seen, heard, understood, and fully accepted. The work is to give those wounded aspects a "voice," to express what was inexpressible before. It enables the natural process, that was halted when the feelings were first experienced, to complete.

If that younger aspect of yourself is going to have a different experience of those feelings, they have to be held in a safe container, allowed to express completely, and be experienced from the perspective of your "now" mind. Where before your mind saw these feelings as intolerable, allowing yourself to fully feel them and come through it unharmed gives you a new experience of them, a *corrective experience*.

Corrective experiences like this are often challenging and require an effort of will coming from strong, clear intentions to heal, to stick with it. Sometimes a single occurrence is enough to bring about the kind of deep, authentic expression that can make a significant change in your experience of life. Other times you have to revisit it time and time again, sometimes coming at it from many different angles, to feel complete with it.

One of the biggest barriers to this kind of work is the intensity of the emotions that can be released and the unquestioned felt sense of reality they create. Moving into the emotions associated with a traumatic experience can at times seem impossible because it *feels* impossible. Understanding how meaning and emotion shape your experience of everything can empower you to have choice in going into the dark and scary places of your psyche.

Meaning and Emotion

One hundred percent of any real growth and emotional healing you'll ever experience amounts to a shift in your perspective — in other words, a change in the meaning that your mind assigns to your experiences. That meaning creates your felt sense of reality. When the meaning attributed to something changes, how you *implicitly feel* about it and *instinctively respond* to it changes. This is especially true with the meaning that determines how you perceive and feel about yourself.

Learning to be aware of the way your mind interprets experiences, assigns meaning, and then triggers emotions to navigate you through those experiences is crucial for personal growth in general and medicine work specifically. Good, bad, right, wrong, safe, dangerous, positive, negative, and so on; that assigned meaning isn't necessarily reality, but rather the felt sense of it. It's the emotional response your body gives, based completely on what your mind interprets the experience to mean *for you*.

Sometimes, that response can be obvious, like the feeling of needing to use caution near the edge of a cliff. Most often it is so subtle you aren't consciously aware of it. And responses don't just occur with big events, but with everything you experience. Because of this, the meaning your mind assigns and the resulting emotions that are triggered are the autopilot navigating your life. Left unchallenged, this "emotional autopilot" has nearly absolute control over your experience. Understanding how it works and observing the myriad ways it operates in your life is the key to learning how to reprogram it. This is personal growth.

When I was a kid, I loved playing with magnets and was fascinated with the invisible forces that I could feel at work. I was especially intrigued by how they would pull towards each other when I held them facing each other, but if I flipped one over, they would repel away from each other.

Many years later I had an insight that radically changed my understanding of what my experience of life is and how it works: the meaning that my mind attributes to anything that I experience makes it "magnetic" for me. And my emotions are the pushing and repelling forces that move me in relation to it.

If I perceive something as potentially beneficial or positive for me, my emotional magnet pulls me towards that experience. I feel positive or pleasurable emotions, a comfortable or hopeful feeling, and move towards whatever appears to be the cause of those feelings. If I perceive something as potentially diminishing or negative for me, a sense of discomfort, that magnet is "flipped over," and there is a repelling force pushing me away from it. The more intense the feelings about an experience are, the stronger that magnetic force is and the more strongly I'm influenced by what I feel.

We aren't the pointy-eared Vulcans from *Star Trek* who operate only by logic. We are animals that operate first and foremost by how experiences feel to us. It's this navigation that happens automatically, and much faster than any cognitive processing (thinking) ever could, that enables us humans to live long and prosper. It is *implicit* learning based on experience. You don't have to think it, you just feel the implied "truth" of it for you.

Under ideal circumstances, meaning gets assigned to something when its importance to you is clear. Then, you use that meaning to help you navigate life without having to reassess that same thing each time you encounter it. Burn yourself once by accidentally touching something hot, and how you relate to hot objects like a pan just out of the oven is changed forever. Sure, accidents can and will happen. But mostly you are more cautious and aware, and hurt yourself less often because of it. This kind of meaning-based understanding and emotional magnetism is helpful.

Of course, this is also a radical oversimplification of how meaning works. The inner realities of people are layers of interconnected webs of meaning in an incredibly complex system that has everything to do with how a person's life is experienced.

We've most all experienced in ourselves and others the seemingly paradoxical situations where people are drawn towards situations that may be detrimental or even dangerous for them. An easy example is those who had abusive parents being drawn into abusive relationships. They are drawn to this apparently negative situation because deep inside they have a felt sense of safety in the familiar or the unconscious promise of resolution around painful, unresolved issues or traumas. They often feel an intense attraction, a magnetic pull, towards the personality traits, insecurities, and unhealed wounds that their abusers had. It *feels* like this time it will work, it *feels* positive and full of promise. So often people are drawn back to the original pain in the unconscious hope of a corrective experience so the early relational trauma can be healed. Maybe this time they can get it right.

In my earlier relationships, I was unknowingly pulled into them to re-create the painful aspects of the dysfunctional relationship with my mother. My unconscious hope was that this time the person I loved would see how much I was hurting, that they would care, and that I could be "fixed" by this person. In a misguided way, I was being magnetically pulled towards something that felt positive.

There's another aspect also, which is the biological imperative of the brain. We are drawn to pay attention and react strongly to negative stimuli, because the brain is always on the alert to keep us safe. People that suffer from developmental trauma tend to have highly reactive nervous systems, are hyperalert for danger, and remember negative stimuli more clearly than people without those experiences do. It is all so incredibly complex. This is why developing the willingness and ability to be deeply self-aware and self-honest is so critical to any true personal growth and healing.

Corrective Experiences

What happens when the meaning assigned to something isn't helpful or even accurate? As a kid I ate a piece of candy, expecting it to be watermelon-flavored and sweet. But the taste I experienced was sour and tart and I felt something was wrong with the candy. I spit it out with a grimace, looked at the wrapper, and saw that it was actually raspberry flavored.

From that day forward, the taste, smell, and even the look of raspberries brought up the feeling that they were undesirable for me, and I was repelled away from experiencing them so subtly that I never even thought to question it. This was just a part of the texture of my felt sense of reality. It felt real that raspberries tasted bad and that I didn't want them.

Years later, I gave myself a corrective experience of eating raspberries fresh with the clear intention of trying them with an open mind, even though I had pretty strong preconceived notions of what it would be like. I enjoyed them! That experience began to change the meaning I'd assigned to raspberries and thus the feelings that would come up when I encountered them.

It took several intentional corrective experiences to fully change how my body automatically responded to raspberries. It was a process of reminding myself that I liked them in the face of a lingering sense of wrongness that arose when I considered eating some. In this one simple way, I changed my experience of life to be more in alignment with what is authentic for me. I'm now emotionally pulled towards an experience that I genuinely enjoy, the taste of fresh raspberries, rather than being repelled away by feelings based on one old unpleasant experience.

This same process can work with any sense of implicit meaning you might have. It's all available to be questioned and, if appropriate, updated through corrective experiences. Sometimes corrective experiences involve actual physical experiences, like eating raspberries or intentionally choosing to spend time near calm, friendly dogs to help overcome a fear of them.

At other times, corrective experiences can involve evaluating an implied meaning from a higher, clearer perspective. These kinds of insights happen frequently and spontaneously in all kinds of psychedelic experiences.

And yes, changing the meaning and thus the felt sense of reality for something like raspberries is relatively simple compared to mending the emotional wounding of trauma. As the emotional intensity increases, it all becomes much more challenging. This is where psychedelic medicine work comes into play.

For example, I had a miserable interaction with a construction contractor who did poor work at my home. He wouldn't fix the issues, and we ended up in a lawsuit. I felt frustrated, angry, and self-righteous because I felt that he was repeatedly lying in an effort to get out of being responsible for the defects in his work. I'd lie awake at night with these thoughts circling endlessly in my mind, clenching my teeth until my jaw hurt. I was so angry because it felt real that he was doing this *to me*. I understood conceptually that it wasn't actually about me and that it was him coping with a stressful situation in the only way that he knew how. But it didn't feel that way. The felt sense of reality, the meaning my psyche attributed to this experience, was far different from my ideas about it.

I could have clung to that concept as a truth and bypassed the reality of how I felt about it by burying it deep inside. People bypass the truth of themselves in favor of ideas about how they are supposed to think and feel all the time. But that's not productive, and I knew that there was a valuable lesson in this for me.

I never intentionally took this issue into any medicine work sessions, though several times I found my mind spinning round and round about it as I was coming down from the medicines. When in this loop, I was consumed by it. The meaning my mind assigned to the experience blended into me completely, and I couldn't see or feel anything but that. There was no room for a different point of view at all.

Given the intensity of the feelings being triggered, I could tell my response was tied to something core in me and not actually about this issue with the contractor at all. I had to give it the time it needed to soften, so a space could be created around it to make room for a different perspective.

On the comedown of a journey on ketamine and mushrooms, I caught a break. I felt the anger surfacing and the loop trying to start. I knew that the anger was my gateway into whatever was underneath, so I took big, slow breaths from deep in my abdomen as I did my best to relax my body and welcome the feeling of anger, allowing it to expand and express.

With several minutes of deep breathing and my medicine guide massaging the vagal nerves on the sides of my neck, my body relaxed. I could feel the energy of the anger release and open into a deep place of fearful anxiety.

The feeling that came through was that if the contractor was to get away with taking advantage of me by lying, then I would be in a helpless, powerless position, left vulnerable and diminished. My anger was a defensive reaction, moving me to fight tooth and nail to get out of feeling so vulnerable to another's perceived abuse. I was in an intense struggle to not be a victim.

As that space opened, I started an intense, cathartic release of energy in the form of movement. I surrendered, allowing my body to move however it needed to. I found myself screaming, *You're a liar!* over and over again. Clearly this was coming from a much older wounded place, a much younger me, and I let it all vent out until it felt complete. I had vague memories float up of someone having been abusive to me and then lying about it by acting like they hadn't done anything wrong. It felt like this had happened many times, but I was seeing shadows through a frosted glass door and didn't yet know the details. Still, I could feel the intense frustration, rage and shame I'd felt at the time.

As the catharsis felt like it was coming to its natural conclusion, and the intensity of the feelings diminished, I began to perceive my interaction with the contractor more clearly. Once I gained some clarity and settled down, I was willing to entertain a settlement to bring it all to a close and put it behind us.

Initially, I had a felt sense of threat, vulnerability, and victimization in my conflict with the contractor. This kept me needing to fight my way out of it, to win, in order to be safe. I could remember many situations in my life when someone's dishonesty had triggered the same fear-driven, angry response in me. Now, by fully experiencing those feelings, by not resisting how terrible they made me feel, a space opened up, and I was able to see things from a less defended place that gave me a new perspective on it.

That new perspective, the insight, *was* the corrective experience. It immediately shifted the meaning assigned, not just to this current experience but to any time I felt I was being affected by someone's dishonesty. Instead of launching into a survival response, now I might get annoyed, but I'm able to deal with the actual situation in a more rational way. In subsequent medicine work journeys, I would go deep to explore and heal the underlying trauma that had been inadvertently triggered by my experience with the contractor.

Meaning about Feelings

Allowing the expression of an emotionally wounded, heavily defended place is so challenging and seemingly impossible because of a sense of implied menace in feeling it. The felt sense of reality, the meaning, is one of extreme threat, even if you can't say exactly why. That sense is so powerful that normally there isn't even a question of whether it is justified, any more than there's a question of whether you should step out in front of a moving bus.

Unhealed emotional wounds created by traumatic experiences are a snapshot in time, as with trauma or PTSD, or a collage of snapshots that have accumulated over time, as with Complex PTSD or developmental trauma. Such wounds retain the full emotional experience at the peak of when it seemed to be a threat to your very survival. When an emotional wound is fully triggered, you are there again, with that state of mind and intense flood of emotion fully embodied, and once more feeling that sense of imminent threat. Healing requires the bravery to step out in front of that metaphorical bus and fully experience the emotions in that wound.

Resistance to allowing an emotional wound to express often isn't at the level of thought. Frequently it's instinctive, the way the fear of getting too close to a rattlesnake is instinctive. Your body understands not to do it, perceiving this as a matter of survival. On a day-to-day basis, you may not recognize the feeling as fear — it's not like hearing a burglar in your home late at night. Rather, the feeling lurks just outside your conscious awareness. You are simply steered clear of engaging the wound by feelings of discomfort or anxiety, or you are steered towards something else by a sense of need or desire until the threat of triggering those feelings is averted.

Trauma can heal when you allow yourself to experience the emotional wounds fully and completely. You give yourself corrective experiences for those emotional states by surviving something your body has labeled as too dangerous to survive. Sometimes this can be done all at once, though often when the emotions are really intense, the healing comes by feeling them a little at a time over multiple experiences. Each new corrective experience makes it possible to go in a bit deeper the next time. When your defenses are too powerful and you can't get access with other approaches, like therapy or expansive psychedelic use, medicine work can help.

Empathogenic psychedelics, like MDMA, that engender a potent feeling of well-being, openness, and safety, can make this kind of expression of emotional wounds not just possible but sometimes as easy as having a conversation with a friend about it. This is why empathogens, when properly used, can be so empowering in healing many kinds of trauma, including PTSD, Complex PTSD, and developmental trauma. Empathogens have helped many people find a safe space in which to openly express the feelings that they felt during the horrors of war, when witnessing or experiencing violence, exploitation, or abuse, and in the midst of many other traumas — allowing them to begin the process of accepting, releasing, and healing.

CHAPTER 6

MEDICINE WORK

Traditional psychotherapy and expansive psychedelic use have their place and can have significant benefits when used as tools for healing. I use the tools and skills I learned and developed in talk therapy all the time in and out of medicine work to this day. But true medicine work takes things to a radically different level. The goal is not to seek out elevated experiences, insights, or understandings, though these do come regularly in the process. Rather, your sincere, honest intention is to go deep into yourself, no matter what you might encounter, in the service of healing and becoming more authentic and whole. In medicine work, you can have access to those depths if that is what you really want. It is ALL there for the asking. Piece by piece, layer by layer, you navigate your way inward. Everyone's process and path into their depths is completely unique to them.

I know this can be intimidating. It may even seem impossible when you first consider going into your own deep, dark places. But trust me when I tell you that it *is* possible, and that navigating through the resistance to feeling into those dark places is the hardest part.

Sometimes there is indeed a significant amount of fear to work with and surrender to, especially around trauma. Deep breathing into the abdomen while inviting the fear rather than rejecting it can enable it to flow right through you. Once it starts moving, it feels only like a flow of energy and is no longer scary at all. It was only scary when you were on the outside looking in and resisting. Healing emotionally will happen when you stop blocking the natural process of it out of fear. That's all that this really is.

I'd like to be clear that not all psychedelic healing work or medicine work is hard or scary. I've had many deep sessions that were peaceful and beautiful. The key that unlocks your innate ability to make true healing possible is your honest, clear intention to be open to whatever needs to be expressed, felt, or seen, no matter what it is. This intention is your commitment to yourself, your gift to yourself, as you open to allowing yourself to heal.

The Medicine Work Experience

Especially early on, medicine work can be a big experience that feels like a ride down a fast-running river complete with waterfalls, rapids, and sometimes big rocks. Emotional energy will break loose and bubble up to be experienced and expressed. Your clear and honest intentions for the journey operate the tiller, normally without any conscious awareness on your part.

It's always interesting to have flashes of understanding when you see this happening, as it's happening. But mostly you are just along for the ride, and what a ride it is! Still, your normal defenses will, necessarily, have influence over the process, though not nearly as much as in your everyday waking state. Layer by layer, you peel the onion as you work your way inward. With the help of a good, qualified guide, you can handle anything that needs to come up.

My first guided medicine journey on MDMA was incredible. It was my third experience of guided psychedelic healing work ever. I had been fasting, and I was excited, intimidated, and more than a little bit anxious and fearful when we met that morning. I was shaking as we sat on the floor facing each other to settle in and review my intentions for myself, as well as my guide's intentions for himself and for me that day.

During our calls before the session, I had gained clarity that the desire driving me into this work was to stop living such an isolated, lonely life. My intention for the day was to surrender and allow whatever needed to happen, to feel whatever needed to be felt, and express whatever needed to be expressed for me to move towards being more open and available to connect with others.

My guide burned some sage, and we took turns "sageing" ourselves by passing the smoldering bundled leaves around ourselves, fanning the smoke with our hands to guide it to each area of our bodies. Burning sage is the official start and close of a medicine work session — any thoughts, feelings, or concerns outside of my intentions for the session are to be carried away on the smoke. I don't have any beliefs about what this actually does energetically or spiritually. I accept that there is much that I don't understand or know, and I simply find the ritual to be helpful and an important part of the process.

My guide started some gentle instrumental music as I took 175 milligrams of MDMA, considered a pretty big dose, and lay back on the comfy mat and pillow with an eye mask on. He asked me to tell him when I started to feel the medicine kick in. When I did, he asked if he could do some body work to get things moving. I agreed and felt him touching my feet as he struck a tuning fork against his leg and then touched it to the ends of each of my toes in turn. I could feel the vibrations up my entire leg and then through my whole body. Once done, he picked up my feet together and gently swayed them back and forth for a few minutes. He then repeated the tuning fork process on the ends of my fingers, on my sternum, chin, between my eyebrows, and on the top of my head.

What happened next was amazing. It was like the felt sense of the intensity of the medicine went from a two to a ten. The flow of energetic sensations exploded throughout my body, and my legs started kicking so fast it felt like they were vibrating against the mat. In the session, my legs were moving, my arms were flailing around, and my head was rolling side to side as I made sounds from deep in my chest. My guide let me know that this is how trauma is released from the body, and it truly felt like it, as if an unblocking was happening, and pent-up and suppressed life was flowing freely and naturally through me. I had the bodily realization that we don't contain life energy, we are the flow of it.

As the intensity of the energetic release subsided, I found myself speaking out loud. I spoke in a free association expression of thoughts, memories, hurts, things that I felt shame about, and some of my desires. I wasn't speaking to my guide so much as I was aware of him witnessing this expression with loving acceptance. And I wasn't thinking about what I was saying or trying to say anything specific at all. It was an unfiltered, unorganized flow of words and feeling coming from deep within as I was surrendered to and witnessed the process.

MDMA can be dehydrating, and so my guide was there to gently pour water into my mouth whenever I asked for a drink. He did this so I wouldn't have to take off the eye mask and navigate my environment, which would have taken me out of the deep medicine experience. I laughed with him that I felt like a baby bird being fed by its mother, and his care for me in such a vulnerable state provided another vital layer of deep healing that I'd been unknowingly needing my whole life. I was able to have an experience of not only being cared for, but of feeling worthy of that care as well.

Having grown up without a father or any real father figures, feeling real care, compassion, and empathy from a man was new to me. Had I known this was going to be a part of the work beforehand, I would have felt uncomfortable and shameful, and would have resisted it. I wouldn't have let it in. But instead, with the MDMA, I was able to accept this as the simple kindness and care from another human being that it was.

Around two hours after I'd first felt the medicine coming on, I was offered and accepted a fifty-milligram booster of MDMA. The timing was perfect, and the added dose blended seamlessly into the overall experience, extending the medicine experience for me to work for a couple of hours longer. As the medicine eventually started to wear off, I felt the dreaded comedown feeling of MDMA, as if emotionally I were being punched in the gut or had just received bad news. This caused me to instinctively and violently clench both mind and body, caving in on myself to get away from the feeling.

I curled tightly into a fetal position and told my guide that I was feeling really ashamed and stupid for having been so open, so exposed. It was the first time I made the connection that the painful and unpleasant comedown feeling, that I'd experienced so many times before in recreational and expansive use, was actually shame.

Learning and Healing

At some point early in my life, being emotionally open and available to others had been assigned the meaning, *This is a threat and is dangerous.* My emotional openness was now triggering feelings of fear and shame to repel me away from that state and back into an emotionally closed-off state, one that my psyche perceived to be safe.

In that moment, I saw how pervasive this shame was in my everyday life and the power it held to limit my experience of life in a misguided effort to keep me safe. Shame was also the source of the "depression" I'd suffered through my entire adult life. What had been labeled depression was actually a collapsing inward so as to not be too exposed, a response that fought in opposition to my instinctive need to be open and connect with other people.

I wanted desperately to run away and hide where my guide couldn't see me. I felt the intense burning sensation of shame, as if I'd just spent the last several hours doing something disgusting and wrong, which he was going to judge and hate me for. Observing my distress, he encouraged me to breathe deeply into my abdomen and sat next to me with his hand gently over my solar plexus, where I was feeling the most intense part of the shame. I alternated back and forth many times between closing off to feel safe, and then to breathing deep and finding the courage to open again. It was one of the hardest things I've ever done. Again and again, I closed and then opened again, each time with my guide holding a loving, open space where all of it was welcome, both the terrified little boy and his shame.

As I was coming back to a sober state and started to close up once more, the little boy within me was pleading to not be locked away in the dark again, buried alive under a mountain of shame. Instinctively, the adult me told him I understood what he was feeling and that he was welcome to come out any time he wanted, that I would keep working hard to help him heal so he could be free always. This promise formed the basis, the underlying intention, of all of my future medicine work.

In subsequent medicine journeys, as the medicines were wearing off and that shame was becoming triggered, I had a new choice. I could either close off or focus on my breathing from deep in my abdomen and surrender to the full expression of it. When I made the choice to allow the shame to flow through me instead of resisting it, once the shame released, I was able to have an experience of that vulnerable little boy within me being more free — not when I was deep in a psychedelic experience but rather at a time when I would normally be closed off.

With both my adult self and a compassionate and loving guide there to reflect back to the little boy that he was wanted and welcome, he was again and again given corrective experiences. These helped him build the confidence and understanding he needed to start feeling less like a prisoner within me, too vulnerable to be exposed to others. These experiences started the process of him opening up and integrating back into the whole of me. I slowly began learning a new felt sense of reality where it was safe for me to be open and emotionally available to other people.

It has taken me many medicine work sessions to arrive at this place from a variety of different angles. But the steady progress of healing has yielded a multitude of dramatic benefits in my life. These include a new level of relaxation emanating from the core of me, as well as trust in the flow of life and my ability to navigate it. It has also led to a blossoming in my desire and willingness to connect with others and an explosion of creative expression, some of which took the form of writing this book.

My healing process is ongoing and continues to evolve. Some emotional wounds from later in life can be relatively quick to show real progress in healing, and those from earlier life traumas can often take more time and effort to work through. But each and every step brings profound shifts in perspective that continue to expand what is possible for me.

Building Experience and Skill

As you progress in developing discernment of the subtle experiences in the medicine work space, your conscious awareness and effort of will come increasingly into play. You can see what was unconscious before, but clearly visible now, when your defenses are moving you away from entering certain areas or experiencing specific feelings. You can feel that something is there, and that you don't want to go there.

With more time in the medicine space, you start to be able to make choices that arise from the deep wisdom that we all possess. You'll feel the defense mechanism of fear, dissociation, anger, etc. being activated, and instinctively you'll know it to be guarding a place holding memories or emotions marked as too dangerous to experience. This isn't from "thinking," but rather from awareness of the truth of it. And then at some point, you'll become aware of the choice coming from deep within to move **you**, the center of that awareness, into that space — or not — to experience and give it expression — or not. When you get to this point, you've taken your medicine work to the next level.

I'm still regularly surprised how much this continues to develop in me. I'd been experiencing the process for a few years, when one day I stumbled into a whole new realm of possibility in the face of deeply entrenched defenses that previously had made moving into certain areas seem impossible.

I'd had a big, powerful medicine journey with a guide that day. I had taken ketamine and 3-MMC along with a strong dose of 2C-B at the start of the comedown. By the end of the session I was exhausted both physically and mentally.

When I returned to my rented bungalow for the night, I soaked in a hot tub to start working towards a relaxed body and calm mind. As the relaxation started to settle in a bit, I could feel with certainty that something inside of me was still wanting to move and release. Normally I feel this during the comedown of a session and will use moderate doses of 5-MeO-DMT to help whatever feels stuck to move. But, I had been so wiped out by the end of the session that I didn't catch it.

With every medicine work journey, I make a commitment to myself that anything asking for expression will be given the chance. So even though I was exhausted, hungry for dinner after having fasted all day, and desperate to just be a vegetable for a while, I geared myself up for more work.

I decided I'd work with ketamine and 5-MeO-DMT vape pens. I also acknowledged to myself that I was feeling fear of letting those stuck feelings out, while simultaneously admitting I didn't want to do any more work and could easily talk myself out of it. But that would have felt terrible and would likely have left me feeling anxious and irritated for days.

If you have never done real, deep medicine work before, what I'm about to describe here could, and should, be intimidating. Just know that it is advanced and not what most are likely to ever encounter in their own work, certainly not early on. If you have built the experience and inner tool kit to be able to navigate this level of the work, then you'll also have the ability to choose whether you want to go there or not with a great deal of confidence.

But for someone without a lot of experience doing deep work, this can be truly dangerous and should never be tried.

At this point, I was more experienced in true, deep psychedelic work than the majority of the medicine guides I'd ever met, and I took any risks willingly in the name of the healing demanding to happen. In the previous years, I had done many deep, intense medicine work journeys and had become extremely adept at navigating that deeper space. I know the line I can never cross working solo with medicine dosages, especially when layering.

With a few deep breaths, I connected with the felt sense of tightness just left of and below my solar plexus under my rib cage. It was the pressure I was feeling of the emotional energy wanting to express but being held in habitually by fear. I'm careful not to blast in with more than is necessary, so I look for the sweet spot to give that part of me the choice to express or not.

I did a moderate hit and laid back on my pillow, holding my breath as I counted backwards from ten as the drug absorbed into my bloodstream. As the impossibly vast space opened up in my mind and body, I could feel some of the knots of tension in the stillness that are the energetic blockages of emotional wounds, and I could feel the specific one that was asking to express as a place radiating a deeply cold fear.

Instinctively, and before I had any choice, the defense mechanism of dissociation kicked in, and my awareness was pushed away into a euphoric and blissful state. I believe I was thinking of the actress Scarlett Johansson. If one must dissociate, she's not a bad way to go.

Damn it! I immediately knew what had happened, but it happened so fast that I had no choice about it. As I lay there catching my breath and letting the first round settle a bit, I knew I'd have to go in again, and this time make a conscious choice to not dissociate but choose to go into the fear. I really, really, *really* didn't want to do any more work, but I knew that I had to.

I'm not sure how to put into words how hard it is to choose to purposefully push into that kind of fear or how influential the impulse can be to unquestioningly follow the instructions of deeply ingrained defense mechanisms. Historically in these situations, I have had to keep going back in with progressively larger doses of the 5-MeO-DMT, under the watchful eye of a psychedelic guide, until I'm permitted past the defenses, and the expression can occur. Often each new round requires me to muster all of the courage that I can. Sometimes I'm begging, crying, and pleading with myself not to do it. Other times, I'll sit rocking in place, holding the vape pen between my hands as if I'm praying to… I'm not sure *who*…to give me the strength to do what is needed. That fear *is* the next gate, and only by passing through it will the energy of the trapped emotion, the expression of the wound, happen.

But that night I was too tired for so many rounds of this. And so I said out loud to myself, *I have to lean into it, I have to choose to lean into it. It has to happen tonight, no matter what.* The choice to lean into fear happens all the time in medicine work; it's a crucial part of the process. But this was something new, and it was happening at a level of psychological functioning that is normally so subtle and completely unconscious, and happens so fast, that previously I'd never even known it had happened until long after. With this new insight into the process and with that clear intention set, I took a bigger hit than the last time.

As I lay back holding my breath and counting backwards from ten, the previous dose still lingering in my system, I launched into a much bigger, greatly intensified experience. Within seconds, or possibly days, weeks or years — it's hard to tell on 5-MeO-DMT — I could sense that fearful place, like locating a source of heat with my eyes closed. It radiated menace. Something inside of me wanted to pull back and not look at it, to not admit that it even existed, but I was able to make the choice to push into it instead — not with a thought but an action of will that occurred in a fraction of a second, my clear intention in action. There was the briefest flash of fear, and then it moved into a powerful, energetic release.

I immediately flipped over and pulled close the ceramic bowl I'd brought into bed with me, as I heaved with a deep, retching purge for several minutes. Energetic releases in medicine work can take many forms, but with tightly defended emotions, especially those having to do with trauma, it seems as if the body views them as toxic and seeks to get rid of them like any other ingested toxin. At least, that's sure how it feels.

Once that "energy" is in your awareness, the body wants it out. This isn't getting rid of any part of **you**, rather it's letting go of something you've been holding onto that was originally meant to flow through and out of you, but instead festered and stagnated inside of you. I have never felt any of the nausea buildup or the terrible dread in feeling it coming like with a stomach virus or food poisoning. It happens fast, I always want it to happen, and then it's over before I know it. It's a true catharsis, and the felt sense of relief afterwards is amazing.

As I lay there breathing heavily, exhausted and feeling momentarily happy to finally be done for the day, it hit me that I wasn't done yet. I could still feel "it" — something more still needed to happen. I wanted to cry. It was like crossing the finish line of a marathon exhausted, and longing for a cheeseburger and a beer, only to realize there is another finish line, the real one, several miles farther down the road.

I stayed there quite a while, hugging my bowl, and giving myself plenty of time to calm down and perhaps decide that I actually was done so that I could start heating up my dinner. But I knew that I had to go in again, and I made the commitment, I set the intention, that no matter what happened, this time would be the last. It had to happen now.

I gathered all of my courage, sitting up in bed and rocking forward and back as I talked myself into doing it one last time. One part of me, that fearful part, was pleading to *not* do it. He was scared of being brought out into the light, of being exposed even though I was alone. But from a deeper place within me, there was a knowing that this was what needed to happen, it was an act of kindness and love, and that I was giving him/myself the gift of freedom.

I took several deep breaths, renewing my commitment to lean into the fear and this time get what needed to be done, done. I took several more breaths deep into my abdomen to calm my nerves and then drew on the pen, longer this time, and my universe exploded into an impossibly bright white with intricate swirling black patterns extending off into infinity in all directions.

Once more I felt the overwhelmingly intimidating presence of the fear in a tight knot of some of those swirling patterns, like the Eye of Sauron, and once more I chose to move in opposition to my hardwired instincts and press into it. I flipped over, grabbing my trusty bowl, and opened my mouth as wide as I could, breathing in deeply and exhaling sharply through my mouth to encourage the purging of energy to happen. And happen it did, with an even deeper feeling purge, retching itself out of me. Long ago, I'd stopped having anything to vomit, so now it was just the spasms of retching, causing my abdominal muscles to lock up in painful cramps. When it passed, I was left lying there with the cool of the bowl on my cheek and my arm wrapped around the bowl, holding on for dear life.

With cool tears on my cheeks, I heard myself saying, *I'm sorry that I hated you*, over and over again. I could see clearly how I had internalized some of my family when I'd felt hated and judged by them. That dynamic had persisted, a yin and yang of the feeling of being hated and the hating of that part of myself, living on in me decades after those feelings were first felt.

Keeping the boy locked away, in a misguided way, kept him from being vulnerable to feeling hated and unwanted again by others. It was a defense mechanism, a coping strategy, to avoid a child's emotional overwhelm and despair. Left unexamined, that mechanism would have stayed unconsciously active in my psyche until the day I died. This catharsis was only possible with the help of psychedelic medicines and deep, honest intentions to find these wounds and empower them to heal.

For me, with the strength and intensity of my unconscious defense mechanisms, no amount of talk therapy or expansive psychedelic use ever brought about the necessary shift that would allow me to get free from the grip of those defenses and allow such a catharsis. It was like trying to break into a bank vault using sand-paper. This is the true power of psychedelic medicine work.

Once I could get my brain to function again and was warming up a can of lentil soup for a long-overdue dinner, I knew there would be more work around this issue. But I also knew that I'd just moved heaven and earth to help empower myself to heal a core part of my being. In subsequent medicine journeys, I would continue to learn about this aspect, this wounded part, and all of the intricacies of the circumstances that created him as I continued to heal.

That felt sense of reality, that there was something wrong, something worthy of being hated, in the core of who and what I was, sat at the center of all of my misery. The anger that I would sometimes project onto other people and situations had always been this anger I felt towards myself. Once I saw this clearly, I understood that what others had projected onto me as a child also wasn't about me, but rather their own feelings about themselves. I had already understood this from an intellectual perspective for quite a while. But it was only when I actually felt the truth of it from that wounded place, when I could feel it in my bones, that I could allow myself to start the releasing process, and true, irrevocable healing began to happen.

CHAPTER 7

WHAT GROWTH LOOKS LIKE

There seem to be a number of common misconceptions about psychedelics used therapeutically, including that they offer a miracle cure and need only to be ingested for trauma, depression, addiction, insecurities, or pain to disappear. This kind of misunderstanding is what happens when the media or financial interests get hold of something incredible and new — it gets boiled down into something that anyone with a wallet can swallow.

Certainly, many people have experienced real benefit from a single, profound psychedelic experience, including myself. But most often, and especially in the healing of trauma, change accumulates over time.

Feedback about how much I had changed and evolved came to me mostly from the responses of people I hadn't seen in a while. They would be visibly moved at how different I seemed to them. I frequently heard that I seemed significantly lighter, more at ease, peaceful, embodied, integrated, and centered.

I hadn't been looking to others for feedback, didn't ask for any, and wasn't posturing to elicit a specific response. In each case, I was seeing friends or family I hadn't seen in months or years, and they surprised me in how surprised they were by me.

When I pay attention and reflect on this, I can see that my automatic responses and reactions have changed a lot. The meaning that my mind and body have assigned to my sense of myself or my life experiences has improved radically. But if I don't specifically think about it, I'm just me, flowing through my life.

Swan Song

A notion I had adopted as a boy and carried into adulthood as a constant companion was a persistent sense of being ugly and thus not wanted — more specifically, not even capable of being wanted. I believe this notion started as a way for me to comprehend why I didn't feel wanted in my family. I couldn't figure out what must have been wrong with me, and for some reason I landed on "being ugly."

As I got older, this sense of myself as ugly and so not desirable to have around only grew stronger. It came up frequently in my first several medicine journeys. I'd say the words out loud, *I'm ugly*, over and over again, without having it specifically as a part of my intention for that day — it would just bubble up out of my unconscious mind. And then, during one guided session on MDMA, after I'd made this statement out loud over and over again, my guide, with impeccable timing, sat close to me, put his hand on my chest, and with unwavering confidence said to me, *You are not ugly. You are not the most handsome man in the world, but you certainly are not ugly.*

At that moment, I felt in my bones that this was true. As soon as those words were out of his mouth, I had a sense of tiny explosions going off, one after the other inside of me. The sensation started near my throat and went in a straight line down the middle of my body. I had the mental imagery of a building being demolished by explosives and dropping into its own footprint. From the top down, the windows of each floor exploded outward, and one level fell down onto the next, and then the next, and then the next, as this corrective experience registered in my psyche.

In the weeks that followed, I found that whenever my mind wanted to use the "I'm ugly" excuse for me to withdraw back into myself, it couldn't gain traction and so receded again.

And yes, if I had been of a mind to reinvest in that idea about myself, to rebuild that old hiding place, I certainly could have. But I had started the process of healing the insecurities that had made those defenses necessary in the first place, and as I healed, the need for them diminished all on their own.

Now, I almost never hear the word "ugly" in my head, whereas it used to be something I heard or felt many times each day. And when I do hear it, perhaps in an overwhelming or deeply insecure moment, my mind might try to use it out of habit to gain a sense of control, but it's always distant, faint, and powerless.

Changes in Trauma

For deeply ingrained trauma, especially early life trauma, the process of change often requires multiple or even many medicine work sessions to come to a place of feeling like it is resolved and healed. You go through the process, pulling yourself through the layers of resistance and fear, buying your freedom one inch at a time.

The speed at which different issues are processed has a multitude of variables that are unique to each person, but you can "grease the skids" the more you take preparing for your journeys seriously, and by having clear, deeply felt, honest intentions. The process moves faster when you find the will to face and embrace whatever may come up, enabling the fullest, most honest expression possible. You can also speed up the process when you take your integration time seriously. This means daily quiet reflection and movement, allowing emotional expression, leaning on your support to talk things out when needed, and screaming or crying into a pillow if you need to. By doing these things, you are enabling that energy to keep moving, which is the most important part.

Three Steps Forward, Two Steps Back

The healing progression in medicine work is often a process of ebb and flow, like taking three steps forward, then two steps back, over and over again. It's a series of expansions and contractions that seem to have the biggest swings a few weeks after the initial new growth made in the journey and then taper off in intensity over time until you settle into your new paradigm.

It can be disheartening to experience old ways of thinking, feeling, or being coming back after feeling a new freedom. Know that this is a normal part of the process. Those "two steps back" aren't lost; rather, they are now mapped as a known path of travel. Most often those steps are taken again much more easily in your support work during your integration period or in a future medicine work session.

There are plenty of stories about people who had a single psychedelic experience and their life was changed radically forever. This has never been my experience, nor has it been for the many people I've spoken to about their own experiences in using psychedelics to help them to heal. There is a good reason why facilities that offer psychedelic experiences always get their clients' testimonials the next day and not a month or two later. There is a physical aspect to change, including changes to your brain and its neural network, that takes time. In my experience, those "miracle" instant changes almost always fade over the days, weeks, or months that follow.

I've been truly needle-phobic since I was a kid. I had a couple of terrible experiences that left deep wounds in my psyche. My problem with injections or blood draws isn't a fear of the pain. I know that it's not a big deal, and any given stubbed toe is significantly worse. It's more like my brain just locks up; I dissociate and freeze.

Imagine standing with a friend next to a running wood-chipping machine, watching as whole tree branches are fed in one end and a spray of chips comes out the other. Your friend asks if you'd like to put your arm into the machine for medical reasons, for your own good. You aren't scared, you just know instantly that this isn't something you'd ever choose to do. The fear wouldn't start unless someone was actually forcing your arm into the machine. You laugh at your friend's suggestion and wait for the punchline.

That's how it feels for me when medical needles of any kind are proposed. It has taken me five or more trips to the clinic, pacing for a while before leaving, before stuffing down the resistance enough to go get a blood draw done. I didn't directly feel fear so much as a disbelief that anyone could actually expect me to do this. The fear would only come when I actually got myself to sit down for it to really happen. And afterwards, every time, I felt stupid and childish for having made such a big deal about it.

To the point: because of my needle phobia, I put off getting crowns on teeth that had gotten a root canal more than twelve years earlier. But when one of those teeth finally cracked and a piece fell off, it had to be done. I made an appointment with the dentist, knowing it would require a numbing injection. Coincidentally, the week before that appointment I had a 5-MeO-DMT medicine work session scheduled.

Confronting my issue with needles wasn't a part of my intention for that journey. It never even crossed my mind before or during it. But after a day of incredible emotional release, my fear of needles faded away. I only realized this while driving to the dentist's office to get the crown work done. While I certainly wasn't looking forward to it and had other things I'd rather be doing with my time, I wasn't locking up and there wasn't any fear. I remember thinking, *So this is what it's like to be an adult preparing to get a shot...* I walked into the dentist's office, sat still for the numbing injection, and got the work done. I was amazed at how the whole thing had gone so well and had been so easy.

A few weeks later, I returned for the second half of the work, which was installing the new crowns. I wasn't expecting an injection for this part, and when the dentist showed up with the syringe in his hand, a jolt of panic shot through me. Whatever I'd gained before had receded. It took some negotiation after the dentist saw how wide my eyes had opened. He must have realized he was the only thing between me and the door, and I was much larger than him. He calmly walked me through it, and we got the dental work done. But I left that office with a real sense of loss in being able to deal with needles in what I had termed for myself as "an adult would."

With some time to contemplate, what I came away with was that I had experienced that it was completely possible to operate from a perspective in which needles didn't cause me such problems. And while it has never been an intentional focus of my medicine work, a couple of years later my apprehension around needles diminished quite a bit all by itself. I've even been able to take myself to the clinic for a needed vaccination and got it done on the first try. Progress!

Unintended Changes

As I've said before, growth is about evaluating and updating the meaning your mind gives to experiences to change how life feels for you. We don't have blocks of meaning that can be swapped out like components in a computer. We have layer upon layer of interconnected webs of meaning where each element has an effect on everything else. Modifications in one area cause the entire system to be altered. Because of this, the myriad ways that you might evolve and change through medicine work can't be predicted. But in my experience, the change has always been positive, even if it is surprising.

For instance, almost three years after my first guided medicine journey, I was visiting a dear friend, and we were deep in a conversation, intensely in the moment, experiencing being connected to each other. A sudden loud knock on the door broke the quiet of the room, and my friend's whole body jumped and then tensed, a mixed look of surprise and fear on her face. Then, as her body relaxed, I could see the range of feelings running through her as she found her way back from a felt sense of danger to being in the room with me again. The only remarkable thing to me in that moment was that I hadn't had a similar response.

For most of my life, I've had a hair-trigger startle response that would instantly put me into a fight-or-flight mode, with emphasis on the *fight*. I'd have a full-body reaction to being startled that flashed into anger approaching rage, as I readied to battle whatever was the threat. It's a common symptom of those with unhealed trauma. I realized in that moment with my friend that I hadn't felt that kind of reaction in a long time. Before, I'd always had a tightly wound coil of tension at the core of me, ready to be triggered at a millisecond's notice and put me into a defensive position. Now, I could no longer feel that knot of angst like I always had. Even today, I still feel remnants of it, some days more than others, but it's nothing like it was. That startle response was never on my to-do list of things to heal within myself — it just never occurred to me. But as the underlying wounds began to heal, my psyche no longer perceived that defense mechanism as necessary the way it had always done before.

There are more examples of these unexpected changes. Ever since I was a boy, I've always enjoyed video games. As a kid, I loved playing quarter arcade games, and when I grew older, I always had a video game system around. It wasn't unusual for me to play with friends at least weekly, if not every night, when a new, fun game came out. I always loved the challenge, the learning process, and the sense of accomplishment.

I used to have friends come over, and we'd connect our game systems together in a local area network so we could go on adventures together or battle each other, laughing and screaming and enjoying each other's company. Then, once the internet started taking off, we'd battle with each other from our own homes with taunts, laughs, and cries of frustration coming through our headsets. It was a lot of fun, and I never saw it as a problem or as something I shouldn't do.

But strangely, after a year or so of focused, intensive medicine work, I simply lost interest. I've tried a few times to sit down and play, and I find that I'd rather be doing something else. There is no value judgment involved, like I should be doing something better with my time or anything like that. It was a fun pastime, as good as watching a movie or reading a good book, but for whatever reason, I'm simply no longer interested. And even stranger, I miss it sometimes, even though I have no interest in actually playing. Maybe it's just the good-natured camaraderie that I miss.

The same is true with the majority of TV shows and movies. I'll still watch a show occasionally, but I simply have no interest in the vast majority of what is available. I can feel the inauthenticity of the scene. I'm aware that people are acting, and other people are filming it and managing the set. I'm aware of the actors knowing where they really are — on a set, not a real place. At times, I can get myself into the groove to enjoy a show, but not as I could before, and I really don't miss it. I certainly cannot stomach watching news shows or following politics in any amount.

I previously would enjoy going out and having drinks with friends. Or at home, I would enjoy a drink or two in the evenings. Yes, I've gone through phases of drinking too much by myself, self-medicating especially when in a depressive phase. But as middle age settled in, I'd normally just have one or two in the evenings to relax. Single malt scotch and red wine were my favorites. But in the process of my medicine work progression, this too just kind of fell away. I never felt that it was anything I needed to *not* do, when done in moderation and not as self-medication.

There wasn't a value judgment about this either. There were no "shoulds" or "supposed to's" involved. At some point, it became clear that getting better sleep was something I naturally wanted for myself. It became important as an act of self-care and to help me integrate the myriad changes evolving in my life from the medicine work more smoothly. Drinking at night, while sedating and honestly enjoyable, was clearly affecting my quality of sleep, and I didn't want that. So, one day I simply stopped and have yet to be the least bit tempted to pick it back up again. It just happened.

A similar thing happened with drinking coffee. To say that I've been a coffee addict my entire adult life would be an understatement. I have an expensive espresso machine both at home and in my office and have always loved well-crafted espresso drinks. But over time, as my medicine work progressed, my taste for coffee drinks changed. I could only taste the bitterness in them, no matter what it was or who made it. I just lost my taste for it. But I found a new love for really good tea, especially Earl Grey teas, and have tea most mornings as a part of my waking-up ritual.

I have no idea if I'll ever find an interest in video games again. Or if someday I'll want to have coffee or cocktails again. I don't have a preference about it and I'm fine either way, as long as that is what I authentically want to do.

CHAPTER 8

AUTHENTICITY

One of the guiding lights in my medicine work efforts is authentic expression, in whatever form that might take. I try to keep it real, expressing myself authentically, no matter what. Certainly, I am not perfect at this. Like everyone, I still have unconscious notions of what I'm supposed to want or do, or about what I'm capable of, that affects my perceptions and decision-making. But it's my honest intention to be as authentic in my expression of myself as I am able to in any given moment.

It was only after quite a few medicine work sessions that I began to realize just how inauthentic I felt. In years past I'd done a lot of personal growth in recognizing "false selves," ideas about myself that I had identified with. But this, it turns out, was just scratching the surface.

Through working with psychedelics, I not only could clearly see the many ways that I was not allowing the real me to be seen by others, but I also began discovering how deeply distorted my own sense of who I am was.

I had never felt at home in my own body. I felt like I was on the outside looking in on my life. While I always felt like I had a direct connection to my inner experience, I felt one step removed from my external experience of life. It never quite seemed real. The puzzle pieces of me didn't seem like they fit together to form a complete picture.

This was because some of those pieces were distorted by dissociative emotional defenses, coping mechanisms, unhealed emotional wounding, and misguided self-perceptions. Other pieces were hidden from my view completely as what Carl Jung would have termed a *shadow*.

Jung originally coined the idea of the "shadow self" to describe the parts of a person's psyche that the ego deems to be negative or unwanted — parts that seemingly can't be a part of the self that others see, that are pushed into the unconscious mind. "Shadow work" has since been further developed into an incredibly important body of work. Coming to terms with the concept of shadows and how they manifest within yourself is essential to the work of becoming a more authentic person who feels whole and complete.

Only the Shadow Knows

The healing of complex or early life trauma is often a kind of shadow work focused only on specific aspects of emotional wounding. This is most relevant to the topic of this book. But in striving towards authenticity, a bit more understanding of the concepts of shadow work in general is needed. It is incredibly complex; I can only touch on it lightly here. Just know that if you are pulled in this direction, there is much more to know.

Each of us contains both a Dr. Jekyll and a Mr. Hyde,
a more pleasant persona for everyday wear and a hiding,
nighttime self that remains hushed up much of the time.
Negative emotions and behaviors — rage, jealousy, shame,
lying, resentment, lust, greed, suicidal and murderous
tendencies — lie concealed just beneath the surface,
masked by our more proper selves. Known together in
psychology as the personal shadow, it remains untamed,
unexplored territory to most of us.

— CONNIE ZWEIG, *Meeting the Shadow: The Hidden Power*
of the Dark Side of Human Nature

We all have the potential to be dishonest, rageful, vengeful, manipulative, greedy, lustful, cowardly, etc. And the need to belong to our social group, our tribe, is hardwired in the human animal as a matter of survival. When, especially early in life, our caregivers, families, peers, or society respond to our expression of natural human feeling as being unacceptable, wrong, or shameful, we may adapt to survive by hiding that aspect of the self in the unconscious mind. This, too, is a kind of emotional wounding, the felt sense of shame of an authentic expression of the self.

Just because these emotional expressions have been hidden away as shadows doesn't mean that they cease to exist and function — quite the opposite. When we deny those shadowed emotions, they become empowered and can have a great deal of influence, or even at times complete control, over our thoughts, feelings, and behavior. The emotions will be expressed, either by sneaking out, or by building up pressure until they explode, often in regrettable ways.

When you truly own your shadows and welcome them back into the whole of your being, they cease to operate as unconscious subroutines, instead becoming a source of insight, wisdom, and power. Bringing shadows into the light isn't giving them free rein to run amok, as many people fear. Truly owning that the shadows exist and integrating them back into the whole of you is a crucial part of being an authentic person. Integrating shadows is simply being completely honest with yourself about the whole truth of who you really are with no judgment, criticism, or shame.

For example, some people tend to exaggerate or lie quite frequently, and most of the time they don't even seem to know that they are doing it. They are simply manipulating life to be what they feel that they need it to be, using a coping mechanism developed to help control their environment and keep them safe. These people often view themselves as honest people with a high level of integrity. This is how a shadow works — it acts as a puppet master until it is pulled out of the darkness and owned as a natural and authentic aspect of being human.

Living in Fear of Your Shadows

One of my most potent shadows was anger. I recognize that I've spoken a lot about my past issues with anger, and you might be wondering how it would be considered a shadow if I was always so aware of it. This is an important point.

Growing up I witnessed a lot of explosive, violent, angry outbursts and I was on the receiving end of many of them. That rage was the purging of the discomfort of angst, grounding it in the nearest unlucky lightning rod. Seeing the look on their faces and the unreasonableness of their attitudes, I felt deeply that I never wanted to be that, to look like that. My ego determined all on its own that anger was wrong and shameful, and mine was locked away deep inside.

Anger is not only natural, but the full range of its expression is absolutely necessary for a well-functioning person. But since mine was hidden from me, I had no access to use it in a healthy way. Instead, anger would unknowingly build in me until it either exploded or came out passive-aggressively, further deepening my sense of shame around it and strengthening my perception that it was to be rejected within me. Anger manifested in my life exactly as I'd witnessed it happening in my family, if to a lesser intensity.

That which we do not bring to consciousness appears in our lives as fate.
— CARL JUNG

Envy was also a shadow for me. For the longest time, I would have sworn that I rarely, if ever, felt envious for any reason. It was a weird point of pride for me. I had no awareness of it, but in actuality, I experienced envy a lot. I would especially feel it, unconsciously, towards male friends who I perceived to be attractive to women, giving them options for connection and relationships I believed I could never have owing to perceived defects in me I couldn't name or understand.

That unconscious envy would build into frustration and resentment, all hidden away so that I wasn't aware of it. Eventually it would start bleeding out passive-aggressively as deeply biting jokes. I was known as a "ball-buster," making personal observation jokes that all of my friends laughed at in the moment. But they were also always really happy when it wasn't them in my cross hairs.

This is how shadow work works. When I genuinely began to own the reality that I can at times feel envious, like anyone else, then the nature of how it showed up in my life changed radically. I no longer felt the compulsive need to joke around in that hurtful way and haven't done so in years. I'd feel a pang of envy and would then simply ask myself if what I was envious of was truly that important to me. If it was, I'd start to inquire about how I could work towards manifesting that in my own life, rather than focusing on what others had.

Differentiation

As a kid my boundaries were never recognized. It felt like my internal world, my sense of self, was assaulted and overwhelmed whenever someone needed to vent their buildup of anxiety, either directly as rage or passive-aggressively through unrelenting criticism and disapproval. Since I didn't develop a healthy sense of where I ended and others began, for most of my life I felt desperately vulnerable to this. It was as if I were porous, and it was too easy for most anyone's negativity or judgment to deeply affect me, leaving me feeling constantly invaded and powerless to stop it. This is why I developed such powerful strategies for staying physically and emotionally distant from others. It was the only tool I had to not feel like a perpetual lightning rod that seemingly invited the storms.

When someone doesn't have a sense of their own boundaries, they become an easy place for others to purge angst. When a person vents their inner disturbance at someone without healthy boundaries, they get feedback that it was received and has been felt deeply. This often gives them a sense of relief that they have offloaded the pain from themselves. Whereas, if they vented that same thing towards someone with healthy boundaries, they'd more likely get feedback that the pain that they have projected is neither welcome nor acceptable.

The Secret Sauce

I'd always felt that anger was a brutal, ugly, shameful thing meant for punishment. I didn't want it in me. But denying it didn't make it go away. The cure for my unhealthy expression of anger was identifying and embracing that shadow, welcoming it back into the whole of me, tempering it with wisdom, compassion, and understanding. Then it stopped being a bludgeon and became instead the rightful guard at the clearly defined borders between myself and others. This was the secret sauce that started my process of becoming better differentiated and having much clearer personal boundaries.

Healthy anger encompasses a wide range of emotional expression, from the subtle to the intense. It is thoughtful, compassionate, assertive when needed, but never punishing. Certainly, there is a time and place for aggression in healthy anger. But unhealthy anger treats most any situation that triggers it as worthy of an aggressive response, because that's the only kind of anger that can break free to do its job of protecting you emotionally and physically.

When shadows lead us into painful or destructive behaviors, we end up distrusting ourselves. I know that I had a real fear of myself because I never knew how my anger might show up or what problems it would cause. Any amount of integrating shadows helps to deepen trust of the self.

We don't get to choose how our shadows express when we are living in denial of them. This is why it is so life-changing to be able to see them for what they are, to integrate them, and to begin feeling more whole.

Another key functionality of shadows is that those things that are rejected within the self can be projected onto others as something that is rejected about *them*. Those perceived traits in others can at times be triggers, eliciting strong emotions and judgments. Easy examples are the cases of people who are ashamed of the truth of their sexuality who end up focusing rage or hatred, sometimes even violence, on others who freely express theirs. A good rule of thumb for personal development at any level is that if life triggers you, *it's because you have a trigger in the first place*. And that, my friend, is a gift if you can bring yourself to see it for what it is. Triggers are your gateways into the places that need to heal.

Ooh ... Somebody Stop Me!

The flip side to shadows are *masks*, false selves that can make up much of the persona that we present to others. Just like shadows, masks are adaptations we use to show a socially acceptable face to the outside world as a way of staying safe. They are not an authentic expression of the self, but rather a survival strategy. As we receive approval, or successfully avoid judgment and disapproval, our masks continue to strengthen and evolve.

I have a friend who met with a lot of criticism and violence as a child, but he was praised for being highly intelligent. When he did well in school or demonstrated an above-average ability to understand complex ideas or to figure things out, his family would openly discuss how smart he was right in front of him. His intelligence became a mask for him. His personality configured itself around speaking in a highly articulate way and explaining things to others even when they hadn't asked him to. He needed to consistently demonstrate his intelligence for others to approve of it. And yes, he's a smart guy for sure. But there is a big difference in the quality of a person's life between the authentic expression of intelligence and being enslaved to needing to constantly display it for the approval of others.

Some amount of mask-wearing is unavoidable and necessary to navigate among other people, society, work, and among family and friends. Different cultures require different kinds of masks. A grocery store clerk who asks how your day is going doesn't really need or want to know the truth of that question. Your ice cream would definitely melt before you could pay for it if everyone answered this common question with full authenticity. So, we give a slight smile and say, *Fine, and yours?*

while not expecting an authentic answer from them either, pay for our snacks and go about our day. We wear the expected masks of civility to smooth social interactions.

Shadows and masks are psychological adaptations made to enable safe coexistence within one's family, peers, and society. And both can leave a person feeling inauthentic and diminished in the most fundamental ways. As I said, I've had to keep my discussion of shadow work short. There is just too much to cover and it is far too complex to do it any real justice in one short chapter. I only discuss it here because these concepts are so integral to the effort of finding an authentic expression of the self, which is an important part of healing and becoming whole.

Thus far, intentionally doing general shadow work has been secondary to my focus on working through the layers of emotional wounding and trauma, a specific kind of shadow work. But the two overlap a lot. Keeping my mind and heart open to any shadows that are ready to be known keeps that door open for the healing to happen, such as the healing around both anger and envy. And, when healing does happen, while challenging and humbling, it is also deeply rewarding.

Get to the Point Already!

Decades ago, in a talk therapy session, my therapist Taffy and I were doing Hakomi somatic therapy. As I was navigating my way downward through layers of emotion, I hit a roadblock where I was struggling to find the right word to express the next layer. Finally, while feeling and listening to myself, what came through was the term "inappropriate," which was the key that unlocked an important door. Saying this released an image in my mind of a young child, curled in a fetal position, who looked rather like he had been mummified. He was desiccated and fragile-looking but somehow also still alive, if only barely.

Instantly, I had an explosion of energy in my body the likes of which I'd never known before. There was so much more *life* flowing through me — an unfiltered, full expression of who and what I am.

I looked at Taffy and said, *I feel so huge, like I'm too big for the room!* Eyes wide with excitement she replied, *I know! I can see it!* I felt like the energy flowing through me could have caused the walls of her office to explode outward with all of the power being released. And next to me on the floor I had the palpable sense of a piled-up set of armor, like a knight would wear. I knew this to be my everyday emotional armor and I was briefly feeling what life was like without it. That open space lasted for several hours before I started feeling the armor sliding back into place again.

The only other time, prior to doing medicine work, that this child ever spontaneously erupted from me like that was, strangely, during a cab ride to the airport. I was a bit hungover from an MDMA outing with a friend the day before. As I stared out the window during the drive that same image of the child's desiccated body in the fetal position popped suddenly into my mind. I had the same crazy explosion of energy and euphoria through every atom in my body. I started panting, trying to catch my breath with my mind reeling in an effort to make sense of what was going on. I didn't want to get on that plane, I wanted to find a spot with grass, trees, and quiet so I could feel into the space that I was inhabiting. But I had friends waiting for me at the destination and couldn't flake on them. During the flight I could despairingly feel the child slipping away into the darkness once more.

Early in my life, I adopted the misguided notion that an authentic expression of me, of my heart, would invite pain, humiliation, and shame in a variety of forms. Being met with frequent disapproval, criticism, rage, and other hurtful and unwanted attention led my young psyche to the conclusion that something about me was deeply triggering to those around me, although I couldn't fathom what it was. The authentic expression of me, the part capable of open, vulnerable connection to others, was locked away deep inside as a shadow outside of my conscious awareness. This meant that for a long time I forgot that he even existed and lived with a persistent sense of a void inside of me, until that amazing day in Taffy's office.

Many times over the years after experiencing the child briefly those two times, I'd yearned for him, for my heart, to be available in my life — to be living this life. It wasn't until I started doing guided medicine work that this even became possible. It's been a long, slow, and painful process to peel back the layers of misguided perceptions and defense strategies to let fresh air and light into his sarcophagus.

Slowly, slowly, slowly, he began coming back to life. The first indication was the heartfelt admission of the depth of my loneliness and the acknowledgment that I wanted connection and intimacy with others. That desire was an authentic expression from him, and coming to a place of allowing myself to have that was the holy grail of doing this medicine work.

An unexpected and potent benefit that surfaced from starting to unearth this authentic expression of my heart has been a deep craving for creative expression. Over the years, I'd tried various creative endeavors, such as photography. I did enjoy these activities. But they always ended up being more about eliciting approval from others than about the expression of my soul's passion. And so, they rang hollow and would eventually collapse in on themselves when the fulfillment I was seeking from them could never be had in that way.

Again and again in medicine work sessions, I would express the need for creative expression that I could feel from the marrow in my bones, as a potent drive to express myself musically. I invested in an electronic keyboard and started taking piano lessons. And later, I even invested in a full grand piano that still dominates my living room! (It has since replaced my Italian sport motorcycle as my favorite possession, but don't tell her I said so!)

Learning music has awakened a latent talent and desire to create and express myself musically that I'd always assumed I couldn't do. I find myself ravenous to learn, and practice never feels like a chore. When my eyes open in the morning, it's one of the first things I think about wanting to do in my day. I enjoy the challenge, the whole process of learning and watching myself steadily improve over time. Music is a new language where I'm learning how to express what it is that my heart has always wanted to say.

Perhaps most incredibly, I have started to sing! My entire life I thought of myself as having a terrible singing voice, someone who "couldn't carry a tune in a bucket." But in medicine journeys, again and again I would find the desire to sing manifesting strongly, even sometimes with me belting out a few bars while watching my guide closely for any sign of a cringe. But after many months of this, I realized I had no idea if I was capable of actually singing, so I booked a consultation with a singing coach.

I went into it believing I was going to be humiliated for even trying. But when David, my coach, had me try to match my voice to the notes he was playing on his keyboard, I could actually hear it happening! Don't get me wrong, it was rough and uncontrolled for sure. But I could match the pitch of the notes and it felt so, so good to express myself in this way. I had a moment of coming close to crying right in front of him because I felt so much joy in discovering this. He smiled and assured me that I had everything necessary to be able to sing on key, and with training we could find out what kind of singing voice I actually had.

By challenging the implicit belief, the perspective on myself, that my voice couldn't be beautiful in its own way, I freed myself to open into a new reality. I'm not tied to any specific outcome about my singing ability. I'm simply driven to find out what my own voice is authentically capable of sounding like. And as I reflect on that, I realize this has always been my goal with medicine work too. I'm driven to find the true tone, the authentic expression, of me. And steadily over time, that's what I am doing.

Part Two

The "night sea journey" is the journey into the parts of ourselves that are split off, disavowed, unknown, unwanted, cast out, and exiled to the various subterranean worlds of consciousness.... The goal of this journey is to reunite us with ourselves. Such a homecoming can be surprisingly painful, even brutal. In order to undertake it, we must first agree to exile nothing.

— STEPHEN COPE, *The Great Work of Your Life: A Guide for the Journey to Your True Calling*

CHAPTER 9

PSYCHEDELIC SUPPORT

When you intend to explore deep healing in medicine work, having qualified support for the psychedelic journeys is essential. Seeking out someone to provide this guidance is one of the first steps in using medicine work to heal trauma. The trust you feel for your guide, consciously or not, has a profound effect on how vulnerable you'll allow yourself to be in the process. This directly affects how deeply you can reach to bring about true healing. Less than fully qualified support will, at best, limit the benefits you can see from the work. And it can easily do more harm than good.

One of the big challenges for those seeking psychedelic support is that these medicines are still largely illegal, which can make it difficult to find any guidance at all. Additionally, identifying someone truly qualified to help you with your specific needs can be even harder yet.

I found my own guides through networking. I either heard about them from friends or simply started asking around, then followed the threads until I found what I needed. Once I found someone I wanted to consider, we interviewed each other to make sure it was a good fit and that they had the necessary experience, education, and mindset to support me in the way that I needed to be supported.

Currently psychedelic support is generally lumped into two categories: "trip sitters" and "guides." Trip sitters simply sit with you and help keep you emotionally and physically safe during your expansive or recreational experience. The term "guide" is much more problematic because "guide," "medicine guide," and so on are used to describe everything that has to do with offering spiritual, emotional, and psychological psychedelic support. Furthermore, there are currently no standards to govern psychedelic support in any way. Everything falls under the umbrella of "guide," but there is a wide variation in what is being offered and the quality of those offerings. Even in the currently largely underground world of these services, there needs to be more accuracy in the naming and distinguishing of the different types of psychedelic support services. And there need to be clear standards on the qualifications for offering each of those services.

Years ago, I built a computer security consulting firm. The misguided air of mystery and indecipherable skill and power that hackers held in the minds of the public felt similar to how "psychedelic guides" often seem to be viewed today.

In the urban myth, a hacker was a genius-level nerd who could break into almost any computer system with finesse and ease and carry out whatever their shady objectives might be. The reality was much more mundane. Many claiming to be hackers were just minimally skilled posers, called "script kiddies," who just wanted to be thought of as special and cool. While their self-image and the abilities they projected to others were huge, what they were actually capable of understanding and doing was much, much less. Certainly, there are truly skilled hackers in the world. They are a minority among all the posers — and even those who are the real deal are nothing like what you see on TV or in the movies.

The urban myths that have been built up around psychedelic guides are disturbingly similar because the general public, and even many self-described "guides," have no idea what is actually involved in providing psychological support in psychedelic sessions. Most people seem to accept that if they have this title and give off a suitably confident, spiritual air that they are qualified to work whatever magic it is that happens when working with psychedelics. This is a dangerous misconception.

Types of Psychedelic Support Services

I'd like to be clear that I am not an authority or expert who should decide new naming conventions for psychedelic support services, or what the qualifications for offering them should be. I can share what I've come to from my own experiences, and perhaps that can be used as one point of view to get the conversation started. What I've shared here is meant to help those seeking psychedelic support in any form to better understand the nature of what is being offered when they encounter it, no matter what it is called.

Modern psychedelic support could be broken down into:

- Trip sitters
- Psychedelic facilitators
- Psychedelic coaches
- Psychedelic guides
- Medicine guides
- Psychedelic therapists

Trip Sitters

At their most basic, a trip sitter is a sober person who can keep an eye on you while you are in a psychedelic journey. Ideally, they have a lot of psychedelic experience themselves, including having navigated through some challenges while in them. They should be open, nonjudgmental, and prepared to stay calm should the person they are watching over become agitated, fearful, or even delusional. A calm voice offering reminders to breathe and affirming that you are on a drug and that it will wear off can go a long way in turning a challenging trip back into a beautiful, peaceful experience. Many calling themselves medicine guides are really just trip sitters. And that can be fine if this is all the support that you require.

It is particularly important to agree on what type of touch, if any, will be acceptable for the person doing the trip. While touch can be a soothing intervention, sexual touch of any kind should never occur, even if the tripper is overwhelmed with sexual desire, which can sometimes happen. That sexual energy can never be met, as someone under the influence cannot possibly consent to it. One hundred percent of the time it would be sexual assault to take advantage in those circumstances. This is true for all manner of psychedelic support, and it's a rule that unfortunately does get broken.

A trip sitter should hold a safe, loving and accepting space for whatever you need to express without getting triggered or inserting their views or opinions into your process. The tripper may speak with the sitter during the session, but it is the job of the sitter to sit quietly and peacefully unless spoken to. Most importantly, the sitter should not play therapist. Instead, they should behave as a loving friend spending time with you just as you are.

Psychedelic Facilitators

Psychedelic facilitators offer experiences that are targeted towards those wanting to explore the psychedelic space. Most of the support offered at psychedelic retreats fits into this niche. The facilitators are there to provide a safe, contained, and supportive experience, usually to groups but sometimes one-on-one. It's often the next level up from trip sitting, where you go to the facilitator and work within the program they are offering.

Generally, these programs are less about doing any kind of specific deep work and are more about expansive experiences, opening to new possibilities for yourself personally or spiritually. And since deep emotional material can surface in any psychedelic experience, facilitators should be properly trained and experienced to help manage any feelings that might arise.

Ayahuasca experiences, when held by properly trained and experienced facilitators, are most certainly meant to dig deep and can be incredibly powerful. Anyone facilitating ayahuasca experiences should be highly trained with many years of experience under a highly trained and experienced mentor themselves. Too many people have big experiences on ayahuasca and then start offering to facilitate the experience for others without any true understanding of the process or the possible challenges and dangers.

Facilitators will often host their programs in beautiful locations that can increase the participants' enjoyment of the experience while also helping to keep the vibe beautiful and positive.

Psychedelic Coaches

A psychedelic coach is a bit like a life coach, except that the psychedelic coach specializes in supporting people intending to have expansive psychedelic journeys for personal or spiritual development. They'll often work one-on-one, but sometimes host groups as well.

Coached psychedelic sessions focus on taking clear intentions into the expansive experience, with the aim of gaining insights and clarity on one's life. This isn't a therapy session, and it isn't meant to be. But coaches absolutely should be trained and experienced in helping someone to manage anything difficult that might come up.

Anyone offering psychedelic coaching support should have extensive experience in their own coached psychedelic experiences and have also experienced much deeper-reaching psychedelic journeys. A true understanding of how deep things can go provides a much-needed sense of scale when working with others. A coach should also have specific training with using psychedelics in this way and have mentored under an experienced coach themselves.

Psychedelic Guides

Psychedelic guides are the first tier of those who are qualified to guide a psychedelic experience that is focused on emotional healing and growth.

These I simply call "guides." They should have done extensive deep psychedelic healing work of their own, have intensive training, and have interned extensively under a qualified mentor of their own. This isn't medicine work per se, but it's taking the expansive experience to a much deeper level that can encourage and safely hold painful emotions as they are expressed.

My first one-on-one guide fit into this category. He'd done years of his own deep emotional healing work with psychedelics and was trained in a specialized, exclusive program specifically to develop these skills. He then moved into a lengthy internship under his own mentor as he began developing his own practice.

Guided psychedelic healing is geared towards setting clear intentions towards the type of healing and growth that is desired. Those intentions are then followed in the psychedelic journey with intensive follow-up during the integration phase afterwards. Given the depth of this work, it's essential that you work with a qualified therapist for support in between sessions.

In this kind of psychedelic work, things can get deep fast. A psychedelic guide must know when to refer a client out and have ready access to properly trained medicine guides (as described below) for clients who need them. They know better than to try to work with levels of trauma beyond their skill set and will always put the best interests of their clients first.

The ideal guide shows up as a fellow human being doing a challenging job because they genuinely want to help. They are authentic, compassionate, and confident, with no need to project an image of being elevated or of having transcended everyday life and its problems. They don't put on any airs about it at all.

A guide holds a space energetically vast and open for whatever needs to express from you in whatever form it needs to take. They offer authentic connection to the authentic you. They aren't in conflict with your defenses or insecurities because they've done their own deep work and don't need to engage on that level with someone in the process of healing. They will be genuinely calm and grounded in a way that resonates from a deep place within themselves, so they can hold a genuine deep space for you to open into.

Choosing a good guide is critical to your efforts. During a journey, you are incredibly vulnerable and can be easily influenced. You don't go to a guide as an authority to give you answers or solutions to your problems. They are there to hold a safe space for you to open, express, and discover your own answers.

One of the most vital roles that a guide plays in a journey is entirely energetic and is based on a deep empathetic connection with the person taking the journey. The guide sets their own personal stuff aside and thereby enables the participant to unfold in their own natural way and to express their experience in whatever way that it needs to be expressed.

They are also there to help guide you in the experience, should you need it. An experienced and properly trained guide is almost always going to have both intuition and an educated hypothesis about what is happening for you. Whether they do or not, the good ones will feed their own curiosity and, if appropriate, form questions for you — not answers.

During a medicine journey on six grams of mushrooms, I was writhing on the floor with an overwhelming sense of shame. I wanted to curl up into a ball, shut down, and hide from my guide, myself, and the whole world. I was experienced enough by then to know that this was my gateway to go deeper, so I told him what I was feeling: *I feel so much shame right now.* He asked, *What does the shame want to say?* Immediately, I flipped over onto all fours and began vomiting in a powerful catharsis. Always ready with the bucket, he was right there, so it was contained. I grabbed his hand, and he held it, giving me support as I purged years of pent-up toxicity and pain. Had he tried to explain to me why he thought that I was feeling shame or what it all meant, I would have moved my attention out of my physical experience and up into my head to think about it. It would have disconnected me from my direct experience, and I would have retreated into myself instead of having such a profound healing experience.

Guides are also there to help you keep the energy moving if you get stuck. That has happened to me many, many times. We hold a great deal of our emotions in our abdomens, and sometimes (with your consent), a guide can do body work to that area to help open the floodgates.

One time I had asked for some help because I felt like I'd stalled in the session. He asked permission to work on my abdomen, and I said yes. Then, as he was pressing in carefully but deeply, I could feel powerful emotions trying to release and my body trying to clamp down on them. The more he moved around in the area, the more intense the emotions became until I spontaneously cried out, *There's nowhere for me to hide!* This was an important reminder of how instinctive it was to protect myself from emotional states that I was conditioned to unconsciously perceive as too dangerous to experience. With the bodywork, encouragement, and many deep breaths, I was able to surrender into allowing the energy of the emotion to flow through me and release.

Having a properly qualified guide is absolutely critical when someone is processing trauma, developmental trauma, PTSD, or Complex PTSD. The stakes couldn't be higher because lasting additional trauma can easily be unintentionally inflicted. The client's healing process can be diminished, stalled, or even permanently halted.

Medicine Guides

Medicine guides do everything that a psychedelic guide does, *and* they specifically support the much deeper and intense process of medicine work. They could aptly be compared to military Special Forces in that they are rare, highly trained, deeply experienced, and uniquely suited to the job they are doing.

A medicine guide is there to help facilitate the true nature of medicine work — healing deep emotional wounds and trauma. They work in tandem with a qualified therapist or other mental health professional who supports the journeyer outside of the actual journey itself. (In some cases the medicine guide is a qualified mental health professional in their own right and can serve in this capacity.)

They are highly trained and experienced in supporting the trauma healing process. Many medicine guides are also licensed mental health professionals with years of experience in the treatment of trauma, developmental damage, and deep emotional wounding. They have a thorough understanding of how trauma is identified, processed in the body, and ultimately released and healed.

Most importantly, they have done their own deep, intensive medicine work. Not just lots of big expansive trips. True, deep medicine work. This work should have continued into a mentorship under a qualified and experienced medicine guide as they learned what it is to become a medicine guide themselves. Anything less and they are dangerously unqualified to operate at this depth of a traumatized person's psyche while that person is on psychedelics.

Psychedelic Therapists

Psychedelic therapists are licensed mental health professionals that use psychedelics in their practices. Rather than fitting into the role of coach, guide, or medicine guide, they practice more traditional forms of psychotherapy tailored to include psychedelics. In my experience, they tend to perform psychedelic work in a more traditional therapeutic setting.

I've watched a video of someone on MDMA, wearing headphones and an eye mask, trying to process PTSD while lying on a sofa in a therapist's office. Another video showed a man in a session with an eye mask and headphones, but this time on a narrow bed with two therapists sitting in chairs on either side of him.

I can see how this kind of therapy might enable some expansive experiences. Some helpful insights could come through and maybe some level of emotional release. Painful life experiences could be viewed from a different perspective, bringing helpful new insights, especially for those who have little or no previous experience with psychedelics.

But in my experience, this format doesn't allow for the freedom of expression and movement that deep healing requires, especially with trauma. Who would feel truly free and safe to yell or scream in a medical office, knowing that people uninvolved in the process are right outside of the door or on the other side of the wall? Who would feel comfortable thrashing around on a sofa in an office as opposed to being in a safe, quiet, and above all, private room on a large mat on the floor with plenty of space to move around?

These things matter because medicine work can be messy and loud and needs to have the safe space and support to let the expression be whatever it needs to be. Anything less, any requirement (spoken or implicit) to rein in authentic expression, can only hinder the process. Trauma is held in the body and cognitive processing can only go so far in resolving it. I appreciate that these legal channels for psychedelic healing modalities have to start somewhere and that some people are seeing true benefits from participating. But traditional therapy protocols cannot possibly contain an authentic medicine work experience. Some thought outside of the proverbial box is definitely required if the true healing potential of medicine work is to be realized in legal therapeutic settings.

Going Forward

As you can see, there are a lot of potential options when looking for support for psychedelic experiences. Hopefully now you'll have a better sense of what to look for to get the level of support you require for your specific intentions in working with psychedelics.

If you are just sticking your toes into the psychedelic waters for the first time, or want spiritually expansive experiences among like-minded people, a properly facilitated group experience could be everything you are looking for.

For emotional healing — like healing emotional wounds, addressing insecurities, grieving loss and increasing self-awareness and self-honesty, among other things — then a properly qualified psychedelic guide is where you'd likely want to start.

And if, like me, you find that you are dealing with powerfully defended, deeply seated traumas and emotional wounds, then you need to find a true medicine guide.

Going forward in the book, we'll primarily be talking about medicine work for healing trauma and my process of working with both psychedelic guides and medicine guides. To keep things simple, I'll just use "guide" to describe both unless I'm specifically talking about something that only applies to medicine guides.

What to Watch Out for in Psychedelic Support

Who are you, who are so wise in the ways of Science?

—SIR BEDEVERE, *Monty Python and the Holy Grail*

So far, we've discussed the various types of psychedelic support and what qualifications anyone should have in order to offer them. This is meant to help you understand what to look for based on your needs.

Now we are going to look at what you'll want to watch out for as you search out your own guides, so you'll be able to avoid the *many* dangerously unqualified people who so confidently offer these services. We are going to get into some detail around this, not to dwell on the negative, but to ensure that you can easily recognize who is and isn't qualified to offer psychedelic support. As you'll see in the coming pages, without this comprehensive understanding, it could be difficult to spot them until it's too late.

I am fiercely protective of those who are dedicated to the process of their own healing using psychedelics. I know firsthand the courage and commitment this takes and how vulnerable someone is while in this process. In my mind, anyone offering support for using psychedelics in the healing process is by default open to scrutiny and should meet a high standard before being acceptable as such. And unfortunately, too many I have encountered do not even come close.

Should some of these self-proclaimed psychedelic guides recategorize themselves appropriately as trip sitters, facilitators, or coaches, then what they are offering could possibly be fine. But, as we'll soon discuss, I've seen too many of these people take on helping others with trauma or PTSD with no consideration of the fact that they are completely unqualified to do so. Even some of the licensed therapists and Ph.Ds who offer psychedelic support fall far short and have no business working with psychedelics in this way.

I do not say this to put well-intentioned people down. But looking the other way serves no one. Harm reduction should be the top priority of anyone who is looking for, or offering, psychedelic healing support.

I've taken many people on their first expansive psychedelic experiences as a trip sitter. Sometimes I would step out of that role and trip too, accompanying a friend, as we explored that space together. I genuinely enjoyed hanging out or going on long walks, having deep conversations and showing them what this kind of psychedelic experience could be like in a safe and fun way. Because I enjoyed sharing the psychedelic experience so much, early in my own psychedelic healing work I seriously considered becoming a guide myself.

But the deeper I got into my own medicine work, the more I could see how completely unqualified I was to do so. I started seeing the clear differences between recreational and expansive psychedelic experiences versus engaging in medicine work to heal deep emotional wounding. I also began understanding the intensive level of experience, skill, and education needed to be able to hold that space safely and effectively and guide the experiences of someone healing deep emotional wounds and trauma.

Radically Unqualified

It is common for people to come out of their early big psychedelic healing experiences with their first words being *thank you* to their guide, said with glowing admiration and deep, honest gratitude. The second thing they say almost always has something to do with sharing this with the world or with specific people who they just know would benefit. That is a beautiful sentiment coming from a loving place. The problem is that from that point, far too many actually start to offer these services themselves.

I had it explained to me this way. Imagine that you had tooth pain steadily increasing for years and it finally got so bad that you went to an oral surgeon to get a root canal. Afterwards you felt the best that you'd felt in a long time. You realize how a lot of other people must also be in pain and you'd love to be of service. So you go online and buy some used dental equipment, read a few books, and watch some videos. Then, you put out some ads and start offering root canals out of your spare bedroom.

Sounds insane, right?

What I'm trying to make clear is that this same thing is happening with self-proclaimed psychedelic guides at an accelerating, terrifying pace. Because it's currently primarily an underground endeavor, anyone can claim that they offer these services with no oversight whatsoever. If they do so with enough charisma and confidence, they'll have unwary clients lining up in no time. I've witnessed it happening too many times and always do my best to put a stop to it.

Everyone wants to feel in some way special, to have a sense of meaning and purpose in their lives, and gain approval from others. But some find that playing the role of a psychedelic guide can be an easy and seductive way for them to get these things. For many that I've met, that sense of validation seems more important to them than actually being of service to help others heal, though they'd never admit that to anyone, even themselves. Playing guide is a way to bypass their own insecurities and emotional wounds, to feel important and powerful. But they are no more a psychedelic guide than an actor on TV is actually the therapist, doctor, or lawyer that they are portraying. Both are just playing a role and waiting for the applause.

It's *easy* to give someone powerful psychedelics and sit quietly while they have their journey. It's *easy* to play the role of a guide and go through the motions that you've seen others doing. It's *easy* to play therapist and offer armchair diagnoses and advice to someone in a highly vulnerable and receptive state. And, it's *easy* to feel intoxicated by the approval and awe someone expresses if they had a profound drug experience and mistakenly attribute it as having something to do with the guide — which happens quite often. That feeling of purpose, validation and importance is incredibly seductive. And **none** of that is what being a guide, especially a true medicine guide, is about.

Nobody offering guided psychedelic sessions can possibly know what might open for someone when deep, authentic expression is invited into the experience. It is when things get hard, when fear turns to terror, or when the client's experience moves deep into pain and trauma, that being qualified to give this kind of support becomes critical. That is when it would be all too easy for things to get out of control or for the client to be further traumatized.

They Graduated from DKU

Universally, the biggest thing that makes unqualified guides so dangerous is that none of them seem to have any idea how unqualified they really are. This is a phenomenon called the Dunning–Kruger effect, in which someone with a low level of proficiency at a skill will overestimate their ability, even assuming mastery. This happens because they don't have any idea of how much there is to know about that subject, so they can't possibly gauge how skilled and knowledgeable they actually are.

This is how dangerously unqualified guides can project such authentic confidence in their skills. They genuinely have no idea how much they don't know about it. And this is just as true for new guides popping up as it is for some that have been doing it for decades. Having been a self-proclaimed guide for a long time or being a licensed therapist or a Ph.D. is absolutely not an indicator of basic proficiency, let alone mastery, when it comes to working with psychedelics in this way.

I met someone who determined that he was going to offer MDMA therapy sessions specifically for PTSD. He did not have any education in psychology or training of any kind. But, being charismatic and articulate, he quickly started lining people up to pay him for this service.

He once shared that he was treating a woman who he said had developed PTSD because her boyfriend left her for a transsexual woman in Thailand. And while that may have been painful and confusing for her, and something that she could gain clarity and resolution around in properly supported psychedelic sessions, by itself that's not PTSD. But he was quick to diagnose it as such for her, and they started her "treatment" in earnest.

Instead of encouraging her to focus on her own experience, the pain she was resisting, and the meaning her mind was giving to what happened with her boyfriend, he tried explaining it away by telling her that her boyfriend was "weird" and that it was all his fault for hiding this part of himself from her, so she shouldn't feel bad. Unqualified guides always seem to be in a big hurry to play at being a therapist, which is never helpful.

Because he had no education in handling mental health issues, he couldn't see this crucial mistake for what it was. He couldn't see that by judging her boyfriend, or anyone, that he was also telling her that there were limits to what she herself could share or express in session or she might also be judged by him. So, whether she knew it or not, what she allowed herself to experience and express was limited to what felt safe around this "guide."

Everything about this interaction disturbed me deeply. This guide was not just unqualified, he was truly dangerous in his ignorance and criminal in the fraud he was perpetrating on vulnerable people. And he was completely unwilling to acknowledge his lack of understanding and skill. Once people playing psychedelic guide start getting approval and validation from offering these services, the cognitive biases that blind them to anything suggesting that they shouldn't be doing it get much, much stronger.

Another self-proclaimed guide I met shared with me a story about a client who, in a session, had an emotional release around his relationship with his abusive father. This "guide" was happy to bask in the glory of this man's tears of joy and gratitude at the end of the session. They both felt that a huge breakthrough had been made, and the guide was more than willing to take credit for having helped that to happen. Though all that he really did was act as a trip sitter with no clue of the larger forces at play.

That same man came back to him a couple of weeks after their session, angry and threatening to sue him for "fucking up his life." The self-proclaimed guide described that man to me as "fucked up" and "playing at drowning." What I saw in that story was someone overwhelmed and clearly distraught and struggling with the emotions that had begun to be released in the session. He didn't have any qualified support or guidance to help him understand that his feelings, even if uncomfortable, were normal and a part of the integration process and that he was safe.

I told the supposed guide that this man wasn't playing at anything and that this is what it looks like when you uncork real trauma. It's rarely (if ever) resolved in a single session the way everyday personal issues can sometimes be. It's often messy with big waves of unpredictable emotions being released for some time afterwards.

A qualified, experienced guide would have known this and would have prepared the client for it while insisting on him having professional support while processing whatever needed to come up. This client could have been helped, but was instead further traumatized by someone who had no idea what being a psychedelic guide actually entails.

Stories like these are why you should not assume a guide is qualified to work with you based on their word alone. They ALL feel they are qualified, even in the complete absence of any reason to feel that way. Referrals from people you trust are the best place to start. Even if you can't get referrals, being prepared with a specific list of questions is important and we'll cover that later.

Their Own Deep Work

When you work with psychedelics to heal trauma, your relationship with a guide is a critical part of the process. Allowing those wounded places in you to safely feel seen, felt, understood, and cared for is absolutely essential.

The same thing is as true for psychedelic guides as it is for therapists and mental health doctors. They can never hold an *authentic* space for someone at a deeper level than they've gone to within themselves. Too many have gotten into helping others to heal as a way to bypass having to face their own emotional wounding and trauma. *Sometimes the call to help is actually a cry for help.*

We all have antennas for consciously and unconsciously reading subtle signs from others to navigate co-regulated emotional connections. If you start on a topic and the other person's voice, facial expression, or body language signals that they are pulling back or becoming reactive, you instinctively know that this is in some way sensitive for them. You learn that it might not be a good topic to bring up or that you should approach it differently.

Our antennas are significantly more sensitive when we are on psychedelics, and if they tell you that your guide is pulling back from you, you'll instinctively adapt to protect the connection. The opportunities to heal will become limited as you switch to monitoring both yourself and your guide for emotional changes to stay feeling safe.

This is where the differences between qualified and unqualified guides really start to become obvious. Yes, someone can have what feels like deep experiences with an unqualified guide. It happens all the time when the journeyer doesn't know any better. All too often these guides are mistakenly credited with the experience that the medicine provided; the journeyer never learns how much more would have been possible for them in qualified hands.

I once worked with a guide with whom I had built trust. During a session, I shared something that was a heavy burden, something I felt a great deal of shame about. I clearly heard his voice tighten and go to a higher pitch as he responded to what I'd said. I lifted my eye mask to look at him. His lips were pressed into a thin line and his face was an expressionless blank. His usual warmth and aura of acceptance were momentarily gone.

Later when I read back his handwritten session notes, that part was written in a much more tightly bunched text, half the width of anything else that he had written that day. If I'd had any doubt about what I'd felt from him in the session it was confirmed in what I could see clearly with my sober eyes. He had been triggered by what I had shared, and instead of feeling safe in having expressed something that had been festering inside of me for decades, I felt even more shame for having shared it.

Because I had shared something from a depth that was beyond anything that he himself had explored within himself, he was triggered and unprepared for his own feelings that came up. He instinctively recoiled from his feelings and by default from me, the perceived cause of the triggering, and in my heightened state of vulnerability, it was gut-wrenching. That old saying *There but by the grace of God go I* should be the first thought in the mind of anyone serving as a psychedelic guide.

That experience not only reinforced the shame I had around what was shared, it also put an unconscious barrier on how deep I would let myself go in future sessions with him. It was a rupture in the relationship that was never repaired.

Psychedelic medicine work is too powerful, and the participant is too vulnerable, for anyone to play at offering something that they don't actually have to give. If a person calling themselves some version of a psychedelic guide, or medicine guide, hasn't done a long series of intensive and challenging medicine work journeys within themselves, then they have no business whatsoever trying to be a medicine guide for others. There are no exceptions to this.

Power Dynamics

In traditional mental health support, spiritual counseling, and any other situation where one person is charged with the safekeeping of someone in a vulnerable position, dangerous power dynamics can sometimes develop. Sometimes people exploit these dynamics intentionally or in a predatory way (as with the well-documented Catholic priests who molested children in their spiritual care). At other times the power dynamics can be subtle, and the perpetrator isn't even consciously aware of it, but the exploitation creeps in over time.

The potential for this kind of exploitation is especially great with psychedelic guides. It's not that they are more likely to want to exploit someone, consciously or not. It's that someone who is using psychedelics to heal in this way is incredibly vulnerable and can be highly suggestible. Couple this with the high regard and deep sense of trust that the client forms with their guide as a natural part of working together in this way and the ground becomes fertile for exploitation to happen, intentionally or not.

People with actual psychotherapy training learn to recognize these kinds of dynamics and how dangerous they can be. But for unqualified guides, their own unhealed emotional wounds can assert unconscious influence over their reasoning and actions, making exploitation much more likely.

I worked with a guide where I would come out of psychedelic healing sessions with a profound sense of gratitude for his participation, guidance, and help. After one session, when it was time to pay, as I was leaving I looked in my wallet. My eyes still weren't focusing well so I couldn't count the money. In a moment of exuberance and heartfelt gratitude for my experience that day, I put all of the money in my wallet on the table for him. It was more than double the amount we'd previously agreed to.

When he counted it later, after I'd left, I received a text profusely thanking me for such a generous payment. He did not question whether it was appropriate for me to make such a decision in the state that I was in at the time. Because he seemed so happy and grateful for this larger payment, I felt obligated to pay that same amount in future sessions out of a concern of disappointing him and possibly affecting our work together.

Over time I started feeling worse and worse about this dynamic. But if I tried to bring up the amount that I was paying, saying that the rate of my spending wasn't sustainable, his response was always that I shouldn't have much farther to go to be complete with my medicine work, not that we should go back to the originally agreed upon amount. I felt trapped by my fear of affecting the relationship and not having anywhere else to go to get this desperately needed help. So I couldn't bring myself to set clear boundaries around this issue.

I don't believe that he was maliciously exploiting me, but he was definitely looking the other way in the service of his own financial concerns. The proper way to handle all of this would have been for him to give me back the amount that I'd overpaid when it happened, stating that this was appreciated but that it was more than what we'd agreed to, and that our agreements around journeys are sacred.

Psychedelic Tele-Medicine

The recent phenomenon of "tele-guides" leaves me confused and frustrated at how anyone could ever think that this could be a good idea. Tele-guides offer psychedelic guide services through video teleconferencing or a phone call.

This is irresponsible, reckless, and dangerous. It demonstrates a profound lack of understanding of psychedelics, the psychedelic healing process in general, and guide work specifically. Tele-guides will sometimes require a friend or family member to be present with the client for "safety." This is absurd and not even close to a replacement for the presence of a qualified guide.

If someone working with a tele-guide has a pleasant experience and never leaves the shallow waters of cognitive processing and a comfortable expansive experience, they'll likely be fine. Having a calm voice to discuss any insights that come up might be nice. But absolutely anyone who knows what they are doing with psychedelic guidance knows you can never, ever know what can of worms might be opened for someone in a journey.

If the client moves into the seemingly infinite oceanic experience of deeper medicine work with no shore or safety anywhere in sight, they could be in serious trouble. Someone chirping calming platitudes from a laptop will be no help at all. Having your well-meaning sister, uncle, or best friend sitting there wringing their hands trying to figure out how to help you as you spin off into a black hole of terror and despair will be of even less help. Offering remote guidance of psychedelic experiences is, to my mind, criminally negligent.

A true, qualified psychedelic guide is a potent physical and energetic presence that serves to hold a safe space in a session, in a way that words uttered through a speaker can never, ever pretend to replicate. That human connection is vital to ground yourself into, should things start feeling too intense or out of control. I've been in that position hundreds of times in sessions, and had my guides not been available with a calm energetic presence, gentle reminders to breathe, and the warm touch of a hand, I would have been in real trouble.

If the client doing the tele-guided journey were ever swept away in their fear, it could escalate into a panic attack or even a psychotic break. Without a safe container and immediate help to be guided back into the body, back to the breath, the mind can easily spiral into intense panic.

What with the help of a physically present, qualified guide could have been a smooth, easy transition from feelings of fear into feelings of pure flowing energy, could devolve into a bad trip. Here the best-case scenario, which is awful, is for the client to white-knuckle their way through it and wait for the drugs to wear off. The worst-case scenario is that they hurt themselves, someone else, or that law enforcement gets involved.

I emphatically recommend that tele-guidance of psychedelic journeys be stopped immediately, with no exceptions. My hope is that those looking for help from psychedelic medicines understand why this route is such a horrible and dangerous idea and why it should be avoided.

Vetting a Guide

By now you should have a much better understanding of the types of psychedelic support, what qualifications a guide should have, and how to spot the imposters. Now we'll cover the last stage: choosing who you want to work with in your healing process and how to interview a guide.

If it is at all possible, meet in person to discuss working together. A video conference can work, but it's not as good. You need to be able to see each other so you can take in body language as well as what they say, to see if you feel you can trust them and feel safe with them. If you don't have that trust, you don't have anything. This is most important, since nobody will truly let themselves be vulnerable with someone who they don't have an authentic sense of safety with. If you can't allow yourself to be open and vulnerable with a guide, medicine work specifically, and psychedelic healing work in general, can't work.

In your first meeting with a potential guide, you'll have a bodily-felt deep knowing, an instinctive feeling, about whether this would be a good partnership or not. Are you genuinely drawn to work with them? Or do you feel a sense of uncertainty or misgivings about them, even if you can't articulate why?

What you are looking for is an authentic, warm, and compassionate point of connection that makes you feel that you would be safe with them. If you feel they are open to seeing you, the real you, then you are on the right track. From deep down you'll know right away if they are authentic or if they are just playing the calm and centered guru role. *Reach out with your feelings, Luke!* You can tell the difference, now that you know to look for it.

Be careful not to rationalize reasons to ignore your instincts. *What if I can't find another guide?* or *Other people say that this person is great*, or *They seem so nice!* aren't good reasons to ignore your gut. Even an amazingly qualified guide that checks all the right boxes might not be a good fit for you and the work that you need to do. Matching personalities and trust are just as important as the guide's qualifications for working with you around trauma and emotional wounding.

If they feel at all artificial, or if you can feel the early beginnings of a guru vibe or teacher/student power dynamic, or if they seem to need to be "the expert" about you and what you need, you should consider looking elsewhere.

Every great guide I've met and have worked with has shown up as an everyday person in everyday clothes with no pretense or costumes involved whatsoever. Those that seem to need you to invest in, and reflect back to them, the validity of their persona, are best avoided.

This shouldn't be confused with someone who settles into "the zone" for doing guide work. This often is an open, empathetic, and calm space. A good guide is quiet both externally and internally so they can see, hear, feel, and connect with the person they are guiding. There is no pretentious posturing or speech; they are soft, open, and available for whatever you need to express in whatever form it might take.

Asking Good Questions

If a guide passes the gut check and feels to you like they have potential, next is to ask some important questions. Often those seeking help will feel shy or uncomfortable asking a potential guide (or even a therapist) probing questions. But you have every right to understand who you are considering working with at such an intimate level. If they aren't open to giving clear answers, that lets you know that this isn't a good fit for you. Medicine work is all about trust, and building that trust starts here.

How a guide reacts to your questions is just as important as anything that they might say. If they become in any way defensive, you'll know you've hit a sore spot and a lack of confidence in what they offer. If they are qualified, they'll have a calm, reasonable response, no different than if you asked a licensed therapist what qualifies them to be a therapist.

Also, look for baseless confidence, like that found in those caught up in the Dunning–Kruger effect and their own cognitive biases. Check your gut to see if you feel like they are being open and authentic with you or if they are trying to convince you. Nobody truly qualified will ever try to convince you of their qualifications.

Here are some important questions to ask a potential guide. With each question, it's important to note both the content of their answers and how those answers make you feel. Does their response give you confidence that you'll be in good hands, safe, and well cared for? In your gut, do you sense they are confident in their answers and that they truly know what they are talking about?

1. What qualifies you to be a psychedelic guide?

This is the mother of all questions, and their immediate reaction and response will tell you a lot. Any defensiveness is a big red warning flag. This question will let you know if they understand what being qualified to be a psychedelic guide even means. If their response doesn't cover experience, education, training and their own deep work, then this should be a concern. However, the remaining questions will help you to understand each of these points more clearly as well.

A common response such as *I've been a guide for hundreds of psychedelic journeys* is a place to start. But that doesn't mean that they have had any real idea what they were doing for those hundreds of journeys. If this is the entirety of their qualifications, then you are likely working with someone with a homegrown understanding of medicine work and psychological principles, and that should be setting off warning bells for you.

2. **How much experience do you have as a psychedelic guide? What kind of experience was it and in what kind of settings? What medicines have you worked with?**

Look for any attempts to be elusive by not directly answering this question. Especially if you are intentionally looking to process trauma, you want someone with a lot of education and experience with trauma specifically.

3. **What education and training have you received that qualifies you to do psychedelic guide work?**

I've heard all kinds of nonsensical responses to this question, from *The mushrooms taught me,* to *There's training?* Once more, you are looking for any signs of defensiveness or avoiding answering the question. Keep in mind that training might not take place in a classroom setting. Working several years under a highly qualified, highly educated mentor can work too for someone with a natural talent for it.

Inquire also about any certifications and licenses that they might have. At this point in time, most legally licensed therapists won't do psychedelic work under that license. Still, it's important to know if a prospective guide has a license or not, as it gives you a better understanding of the kind of education that they have.

It's not necessary that they be a licensed therapist, and as we've discussed before, just because someone is licensed doesn't mean that they are good at it or qualified to do medicine work. It's just more information.

I've worked with medicine guides who are licensed therapists. And I've worked with a talented, qualified guide who wasn't, but who did have extensive training and experience in being a guide, as well as in Hakomi Mindful Somatic Psychotherapy and other modalities. The latter was a great psychedelic guide, but when we got into deep trauma work, his lack of education and understanding for that specifically became evident to both of us.

4. What qualifications do you have to work with someone processing trauma?

A good response would be to tell you about specific education, training, and experience, specifically in working with trauma. Someone lacking this who still feels that they are qualified for some reason is likely in the grip of Dunning–Kruger.

5. What kind of personal psychedelic healing work have you done? And what personal experiences would you be willing to share?

If they talk exclusively about expansive experiences and insights, you will know that they haven't done deep medicine work and are unaware of the difference. If they say that they don't have any more issues to work through (which has been said to me), that's a big red flashing light indicating that they still have deep unresolved issues of their own. This question is intended to uncover how open and honest the prospective guide is both with themselves and with you about the kind of psychedelic work that they've done and the state of their own healing process.

6. What benefits do you feel you have gotten from your own psychedelic healing work?

Here is a chance to test their understanding of using psychedelics for healing and their understanding of what deep medicine work really is. If they only talk about insights, you know that they are amateurs when what you need is a pro.

7. What would you see as your role as a guide in the dynamic with me during a journey?

With both questions 7 and 8 (below), look for detailed, thoughtful, and confident responses. Of course, every journey is different and is ultimately improvised, but there are many commonalities too. Many unqualified guides are winging it, and these questions will likely make them uncomfortable — this will be telling for you.

8. What does a typical journey under your guidance look like?

_____

_____

_____

9. What do you see as the difference between expansive psychedelic experiences and deep medicine work for trauma?

Based on what you've learned here in this book, you should be able to tell if this person has an understanding of this important difference.

10. Ask them to describe how they would approach working with an issue specific to you.

Pick a personal core issue that you are intending to work on in psychedelic sessions and ask them how they would handle it. This question will give you a ton of information about this guide.

You aren't looking for absolute certainty and a checklist. But seeing that they are familiar with issues like this, and that they have a clear sense of how they'd approach it and hold space for you to process it, is important.

Perhaps most importantly, you get to engage them in a discussion and that will give you a good sense of how well the two of you can interact with each other energetically and in dialogue.

What Else to Look For

Outside of the questions listed above, there are important things to watch for when interviewing your guide. You want to see that they are interviewing you just as much as you are interviewing them. Certainly, you want a potential guide to tell you about their background and qualifications. But they should also be curious about you, your background, the issues that bring you to doing this work, and any fears or concerns that you might have as well. If they seem to you like they are selling themselves and their services, then your well-being is not their primary concern as it should be.

1. Are they asking questions to see if you are a good fit to work with each other?

Any guide who presumes that they can effectively work with everyone is someone who doesn't understand working with trauma. That can work for expansive experiences, but not something as highly specialized as medicine work.

2. Do they ask about your psychological history?

If they aren't asking critically important questions about your background, they have no idea what they are doing. This knowledge is absolutely essential before choosing to work with someone with psychedelics. Here are some examples of important topics for a potential guide to ask you about:

- Psychiatric medicines you are taking or have taken
- Suicidal ideation or attempts
- Other therapeutic approaches you've tried
- Past psychedelic and other drug use
- Your current psychiatric support system, therapists, etc.

Working with a Guide

Now that you have a better understanding of how to go through the selection process when looking for the right guide for you, it's important to know how to interact with your guide.

Trust is first and foremost. Just as you must feel you can genuinely trust your guide, they need to trust you too. They often risk much to be of service to those seeking to heal in this way.

Here are some good rules of thumb that will help your guide to feel they are safe to work with you.

1. Don't identify your guide to others.

Just as you need to trust your guide to keep their interactions with you confidential, holding your process and your story as sacred, they, too, are trusting you to keep their participation in your healing journey confidential.

Don't share your guide's name, location, or any other personally identifying information with anyone without their consent. Of course, someone close to you should know who you are working with and when. But in casual conversations, any identifying information about your guide should never be specifically discussed.

I never give out names or contact information for any of my guides to anyone when I discuss that I do medicine work. Occasionally, I'll meet people also interested in doing medicine work, but I never make an introduction to a guide unless I've asked the guide's permission first. I let them tell me how they'd like for me to make that connection. They should always consent to being introduced to anyone.

2. Don't document your guide's personal information, even their name.

Don't write anything that could identify your guide or the work that you are doing on social media, emails, or text messages, even just between family or close friends. Even deleted messages can often be recovered later. Once it is written down, assume that this information will endure forever. This exposes your guide unnecessarily and unfairly and could put you or them in legal jeopardy, even many years later.

3. Use encrypted channels.

In any communication with your guide to discuss the specifics of your journeys, encryption should be used for privacy. There are plenty of encrypted email, text, voice, and video services available, and your guide can recommend which they prefer to use. Many of these have the ability to automatically delete old messages after a given amount of time.

I have a policy of discussing potentially touchy subjects only in person or verbally via an encrypted audio or video call. I never leave it in text of any kind.

4. Don't talk about the medicines.

Especially early on in your electronic communications with your guide, don't specifically mention "medicines" or "drugs" generically or specifically. Many newbies come right out of the gate being specific, even in plain text messages, emails, or voicemails. This is a big red flag to a guide that the client doesn't understand the realities of the situation. Conversations about medicines will come, likely in person or over an encrypted voice or video channel.

When dealing with a new guide, I simply ask, *How would you like to discuss the specifics?* That shows that I know what I'm doing and that I'm looking out for them as well as myself. If they themselves don't know to use a surplus of caution, that's an indicator that they don't know what they are doing.

CHAPTER 10

GETTING READY FOR MEDICINE WORK IN GENERAL

It's important to have a good foundation of self-awareness, self-honesty, tolerance for your own emotions, and at least a basic understanding of your own psychological functioning before starting medicine work. Here, I'll share some things you can do to help get the most from your medicine work efforts.

Establishing Support

Integration, the days or weeks after a medicine work session when sometimes difficult emotions will keep moving and expressing, is, at times, quite challenging. Having a support person who is already familiar with what you are working through, what you took into the medicine work, and what your intentions are, can maximize the benefits you receive from the work. Beginning that relationship prior to starting the medicine work can help prepare you and clarify your intentions. Because you'll have an established relationship with this person, they can move right into the integration process with you afterwards.

If you are specifically addressing trauma, then I believe this support should be from a qualified mental health professional with extensive training and experience treating trauma. Consider seeking out someone who practices Hakomi or another body-centered therapy. Such therapies go together with medicine work like peas and carrots (as Forrest Gump would say). Body-centered therapies put you in touch with the inner experience of your emotions and defense mechanisms. Body-centered psychotherapy helps to develop the observer in you that, much like a scientist looking through a microscope, can watch the processes as they evolve and unfold and enable them to flow naturally without impeding what needs to happen.

Being able to navigate my way down through the layers of emotional experience is one of the most powerful skills that I've ever learned. It is what made this incredible amount of true, deep growth possible for me. Because of this I firmly believe it is essential to build some of these skills before starting medicine work.

Breathwork

Breathwork is a worthy addition to your medicine work tool kit. Its roots can be traced back to Eastern practices of yoga, Buddhism, and Tai Chi, among others. It was brought to the Western world in a big way by Stanislav Grof and others starting in the 1960s. Dr. Grof's early research involved the therapeutic use of LSD, and he could see the immense healing potential of altered states of consciousness. When LSD became illegal, he developed Holotropic Breathwork, a modality still in use.

Today, there are many different forms of breathwork with practitioners doing group and one-on-one sessions. There are also videos online that you can watch to learn the basics, but it's not the same as working with a trained, qualified professional.

If you have never explored psychedelics before, then breathwork can be a great place to prepare. It can help build confidence and comfort in surrendering into true altered states of consciousness. Don't sell it short just because no psychedelics are involved. I have had helpful insights and deep emotional releases with breathwork alone. The hyper-oxygenation of my body and brain always leaves me feeling deeply relaxed and calm.

And breathwork is an amazing tool to use both during medicine journeys when things are feeling difficult, as well as during your integration period to help keep the emotional energy moving. Just be aware that deep emotional material can at times come bubbling up with breathwork, just as it can with psychedelics, and you should have good support available to help you process it if needed.

Keeping a Journal

A journal is a helpful tool in medicine work, documenting your experiences from the first consideration of doing this work and all the way through your healing journey. Going back to review your journal can help you to see the incredible progress you are making. Many times, I've gone back to read my earlier descriptions of overwhelming struggles or moments of despair that are so far removed from my reality now that I've been shocked that they were ever issues.

Journaling can also be a great way to prepare for a journey, to document your intentions, and to note and work through any questions, doubts, or concerns. Keeping notes about your intentions or ideas for upcoming journeys as they come to you will help you keep track of them. It's not uncommon to have a moment of clear insight just to have the memory of it fade away. Writing it down gives you an easy way to keep track and revisit it later to see if it still feels right to you.

During the integration period, especially when things feel challenging, journaling can be hugely helpful. You can regain clarity and remember and refocus on your intentions. It can help keep big emotions in the proper context of your healing process, rather than inappropriately projecting them onto someone or something in your life.

Getting Comfortable with Discomfort

Getting comfortable with discomfort is crucial to any growth process, but especially with medicine work. Most people have habitual, ingrained strategies for coping with emotional discomfort that they are not even aware of.

Eating, watching TV, sexual release, drinking or drugs, and a wide variety of other distractions all can be used to self-medicate and evade uncomfortable emotions. It's the whole magnets and meaning thing again. Learning to breathe through that discomfort and allow those uncomfortable feelings to flow is an essential skill.

As we discussed before, body-centered therapies such as Hakomi are incredible for developing these skills. Slowing everything down and sitting with emotional discomfort as it comes up in a meditation or mindfulness practice is also valuable.

In addition, it can be great practice to intentionally put yourself into situations where you are *safely* experiencing discomfort that will trigger an emotional response. Once triggered, breathe deeply, relaxing your body and mind, and stay with the activity and the discomfort it is creating. Surrender and allow.

This practice can be empowering as it develops both the skill of staying present with uncomfortable feelings as well as the confidence that you can do it. It prepares you for holding space for uncomfortable emotions that will come up in the process of medicine work. It helps you to learn to stay present with your discomfort with no need to avoid or get rid of it, but rather to anchor yourself on your breath, get out of the way, and just observe.

Here are a few ideas to consider for finding safe forms of discomfort to work with. Just remember that while these are meant to be challenging, you should never put yourself at risk of injury.

1. Sit quietly and just breathe

For many people, sitting still in a quiet place without distraction will quickly bring up a sense of anxiety and growing discomfort. Often this will trigger thoughts of the importance of a wide variety of other things that you should be doing, or it'll trigger fantasies for you to escape into.

Try regularly practicing staying present for five, fifteen, or thirty minutes or longer and you can learn a lot about how your mind and emotions try to move you away from the discomfort. Pretty much any meditation practice is exactly what I'm talking about.

2. Deep massage

Massaging out tight, knotted muscles can quickly bring up physical discomfort that can invoke a sense of needing to escape. Of course, you shouldn't do anything that could cause you injury. In a massage session or by yourself, you can use massage balls, foam rollers, trigger-point canes, etc. to keep steady pressure on tight, knotted areas. Breathe and relax into the discomfort until the knot releases. This is an apt comparison to emotional knots and allowing them to release too.

3. Fasting

Fasting can be a great way to learn to be with discomfort. Feelings of hunger can bring up anxiety and unease that the mind will work hard to escape. You learn to allow the hunger and whatever feelings it evokes without needing to do anything with them.

This can be as simple as skipping a meal. If you are someone who normally eats breakfast every day, try skipping it. Watch how often your mind will drift to food and how the sense of discomfort will bring up rationalizations of why you should just go get something to eat.

In adapting to intermittent fasting, my own mind would frequently try the old rationalization: *Well, I'm not going to get anything else done if I don't get something to eat so that I can stop thinking about it.* I never did cave in and eat early. But when I would white-knuckle it and struggle through until it was time to eat, the dam would burst and I would without exception binge like it was an all-I-could-eat buffet at closing time. When I would breathe, surrender, and accept that I was hungry and that was okay, it let all of the tension out of it. Then when it was time to eat, I could have a good, healthy meal, without any urgency, that satiated my hunger just fine.

4. Physical challenges

Another good option is exercise. The idea is to be in that zone where you want to quit but stick with it (as long as you aren't risking injury), staying present with and emotionally relaxing into the discomfort and that voice telling you to quit.

"Holds" are really good for this, where you hold a position such as a plank, deep knee bend, etc. Whatever is safe and doable for you. You hold it for just a little longer than you normally could. When the discomfort arises and your mind employs its various tactics to get you to stop, try to stay with it. Surrender to the feelings and breathe from deep in your abdomen while sticking with your intention to hold for the entire time.

Gentle stretching works in much the same way, such as with yoga. The idea is to find the safe edge of your tolerance and then hold yourself there, allowing both the stretch and the anxiety wanting to stop it. Of course, I don't mean to hold a stretch until you injure yourself. There is a clear difference between the pain of injury happening and the discomfort and anxiety of a safe, deep stretch.

5. Cold showers/tubs

Stepping into a cold shower or dipping into a cold tub or pool is easily the hardest one for me on this list. I hate being cold, and my mind will fight tooth and nail to talk me out of it. It's a great exercise for breathing through the resistance. It's much easier to get into the cold water if I'm tensing all of my muscles, but that's missing the point. So, I do deep-breathing exercises until I can stay relaxed as I get into the water. The work is to stay relaxed (relax those shoulders and abs!) and breathe and allow the feeling of being cold without resisting it. Any resistance is felt, acknowledged, and released.

The whole idea of exploring discomfort is to safely find your edge and stay present with the emotions trying to navigate you away from the experience. Breathe, allow, and observe; lather, rinse, and repeat. This will build not only your ability to tolerate emotional discomfort but also your trust in yourself that you can do it.

CHAPTER 11

INTENTIONS

From the first moment you commit within yourself that medicine work is something you are going to do to heal, the process has already begun. With this commitment, you've given yourself permission to go deep into whatever parts of your inner world are needed to allow the healing that is asking to happen. That permission begins a process much like peeling the layers of an onion. Each layer is the gateway to the next, with admission only being given once the current layer is unwound, expressed, and released.

Your commitment opens new channels of communications within you. You may begin to experience a variety of emotions, including fear, anxiety, dread, excitement, curiosity, and hope. This is normal and something to observe and learn from. It's your first indication of what you'll find as you go inwards, and those locked-away wounded aspects of you are given permission to start expressing themselves. It is from these expressions that your true, honest intentions are spoken.

Intentions are as important to medicine work as the medicine itself — this can't be overstated. My first guide was fastidious about setting clear, unambiguous intentions for each medicine work session. We would start discussing and refining them weeks before we met in person. Unfailingly, one hundred percent of the time, even when I was so high that I had no idea what was otherwise happening, the course of my journey always followed those intentions with laser-beam accuracy.

Afterwards, as my guide and I discussed what had transpired during the journey, we would always review how my intentions had guided the session and what the results of that had been. Then we'd speak again a week or two later to review those intentions again and talk about how it was all settling in with me during my integration period. Clear, honest intentions are what enable medicine work to work.

By setting unambiguous intentions to heal, I am giving the deeper wisdom within me permission to do what needs to be done, no matter what I might face in the process. That wisdom knows what needs to happen to heal me and it is my surrender to that process that enables the unwinding to occur. Watching my intentions guide the process again and again, I've developed a deep trust in this wisdom to guide my life. I've learned to trust in the power of allowing and surrender both in and out of medicine work.

What Is Your True Intention?

Intentions must be expressed from deep inside, not from rationalized ideas, concepts, or beliefs — or to put it simply, not "from the head." If your stated intentions have no visceral connection to the emotional wounds asking to heal, they will not guide your journey. Instead, your *unconscious default intentions* will stay in command. Unconscious default intentions are the same intentions that most of us always have, to not go into those seemingly scary, off-limits places hidden away in the shadows of the unconscious. These are the same underlying implicit intentions that normally keep things safe and fun in recreational or expansive psychedelic use.

True intentions to heal initially come from your body, out of the aspects of your psyche that are calling to heal. You perceive their attempts to communicate with you in the same way that you perceive your intuition, as a bodily felt sense of knowing.

Finding Your Clear, Honest Intentions to Heal

From my own experience, I know I'm ready to start focusing on the intentions for my next medicine work journey when I perceive sensation from that next deeper layer, as if something long dormant is starting to move. It often feels like a subtle (or not so subtle) tension or pressure in my body, not unlike a part of me struggling to take a breath. Sometimes it can be a feeling of claustrophobia, as if a part of me is confined and desperately needing to be free. From another perspective, it feels like a puzzle piece trying to orient and click into its proper place, straining to move from a sense of unease and angst to one of wholeness and ease. I've also had a sense of something out of focus trying to come into focus.

At this point, it becomes clear that this is the next aspect of my psyche that is ready to heal — it's the next layer. It's asking to be released from its prison of fear, shame, or whatever it is, to stand free in the light of conscious awareness and give expression to all that it feels, has felt, perceives, and believes. This is when I start to listen, to *really* listen, because what I hear next is the basis for the intentions of my next medicine work journey.

Imagine standing at the mouth of a deep cave and listening carefully for even the faintest sign of a call for help from far away in the darkness. To have even a chance of hearing it, you'll have to be quiet and still. Taking deep, even breaths from down in your abdomen, you calm your body and your mind. It's a meditative space, cultivating quiet so you can reach out with your listening to pick up even the subtlest sounds, because sometimes that's all that there is.

These communications can come as words, sounds, images, snippets of explicit memory or bodily felt, implicitly held memory, but ultimately they resolve into a clear knowing. These communications often simply bubble up while I'm busy with my life. I try to always be open to sensation from my body and I'll notice that sense of something starting to stir. I'll begin listening carefully and, right on the heels of that, the flash of understanding comes. I don't want to overcomplicate this. Essentially, when you are open to learning your new intention, at some point you realize you just know it, or more precisely, you feel the truth of it.

At other times I can encourage the communication by sitting quietly with deep, calming breaths as I listen for this information to manifest. If I'm still having a hard time perceiving it, I'll often take a long walk with my breath timed to my footsteps, breathing in for four steps and out for four steps, or whatever pattern feels best that day. As I walk, my eyes are relaxed, looking forward and gently scanning side to side with each footstep.

I can get similar results with mindful breathing while driving. Giving my conscious mind something to focus on while in a relaxed state really seems to enhance this listening for me. Eventually, the communications start bubbling up and breaking the surface into my conscious awareness. The key is that the process can't be forced, it can only be allowed.

For example, the need for deeper connection with others was one of the first messages I was consciously aware of receiving as I was learning to intentionally feel inward for my intentions. As I heard this in my mind, I had a clear, felt sense of where this was being expressed from in my body.

Historically, the majority of that feeling of longing was all but completely hidden from my conscious awareness. When I would accidentally have moments of open connection with someone, shame would normally soon follow to close me down and hide that part of me away again, often mid-conversation. But when I could feel that suppressed need for connection starting to stir prior to a medicine work session, it came to inform my intentions for that journey in clear terms.

When put into words for the journey, the help I was asking for sounded like this: *My intention is to help this part of me that feels too fearful to be vulnerable with others to heal.* This wording was specific to what I was feeling deep inside and made no assumptions of what would be found or how things should be handled.

It wasn't so much a thought as a bodily felt imperative. I had a felt sense of this younger me, and what he was asking for, and that felt sense became the beacon to guide my next medicine work session. The words that I assign to it are nothing more than pointers to that felt sense. Lose the felt sense and the words become empty concepts pointing at nothing. This intention was my everyday mind giving permission to that deeper wisdom to go through whatever steps were necessary to affect the help and healing being asked for.

What needs to happen can often end up being far different than what you might imagine, so it's critical to truly speak to what is being asked in the way that it's being asked. Sometimes there was so much fear laced into the part asking to heal that I'd add phrases like, *in a gentle and loving way with nothing being forced,* to the intention. When I did this sincerely, the sense of relaxation around the upcoming work would be palpable.

Letting Go of Expectations

If you tossed a rock into a pond, could you predict everything that would be affected by the resulting ripples in the water? Or how those affected things will each affect the next things and the next things after that?

The interconnected webs of meaning that make up a person's persona and define their sense of reality are far too complex for us to ever be able to predict the end results to any changes within that system. Having rigid ideas about what is supposed to happen, or what the results specifically should look like, can hamper your efforts or completely halt them. It's essential to let go of any expectations and trust in the process. Leave room for something completely new and unexpected to happen from the starting point of your intentions for the medicine work.

Discovering Your Intentions

If you've never done deep introspective or emotional exploration work before, this might all seem confusing or difficult. This is why I encourage checking out body-centered therapies with a qualified therapist or, if that isn't possible for you, on your own as a meditative practice.

Here is a simple exercise you can try, to start learning how to listen:

- When you can take the time to focus and set aside outside concerns, find a quiet, distraction-free place to settle in.
- Sit comfortably and take several long, slow breaths from down in your abdomen while relaxing your face, shoulders, and neck. Take several big, full inhales for a ten count and then exhale slowly for the same ten count, or whatever count feels best to you to get a full breath.
- Take a few moments to observe what it feels like inside when you inhale and your abdomen expands outwards, and then when you exhale and your abdomen relaxes and collapses back all on its own. Intention with the inhale, surrender with the exhale.
- Next, as you inhale, expand your focus to also include your chest, sides, back, and pelvic floor. Your entire torso from the top of your chest and shoulders and down to your pelvic floor are all one vessel, expanding outward as you inhale and relaxing back as you exhale. Imagine the entire space seemingly filling with air to balloon out in all directions and then relaxing back with sensations awakening within.
- Focus on any tensions you might feel as you do this breathing exercise. Give them gentle permission to relax. Imagine sending extra breath there to expand and relax those tensions with each inhale and exhale.
- Take a few moments to feel into what is happening inside of you. Cultivate quiet, so even the most subtle sensations can be noticed. Notice how you are creating more expansiveness inside in the places where you feel emotions, letting in air and the light of your conscious awareness.

Now the stage is set to put on your objective observer's hat, much like a scientist scanning inward with sensitive instruments. You are here to observe only, letting whatever wants to express, move, unfold, or unwind do so. What kinds of subtle feelings do you notice inside?

Name the first emotion you notice you are feeling. This is your first layer, your first gateway to go inwards. I find it helpful to separate the emotion from **me**. Instead of saying *I feel sad*, I'll say *I feel sadness.* The emotion you feel could be anger, fear, happiness, despair, excitement, sexual arousal, or anything a person can feel.

Once you can name the first layer of what you are feeling, it's time to start objectively observing it. Does it seem to have a shape, size, color, texture, even a smell? What can you say about how it seems to you? And most importantly, does it have anything to say? You aren't trying to figure anything out, you are only listening for whatever might occur to you. Remember what I described earlier, about listening at the mouth of a cave? You are getting quiet so you can hear anything that might be expressed deep inside.

As you observe and describe the sense of the feeling, breathe into it, allowing it to loosen and expand with each breath. Eventually, something new will come through as the previous feeling releases. Layer by layer, you work your way inwards as a curious observer. Eventually, you'll come to a place you instinctively know is a wounded place trying to heal. Often this will be the place where you can't go any deeper. Feeling into it for as much detail as you can, while listening for the words that best state what it's trying to express, is where the intention comes from.

A locked-down place expressing fear, a cry for help, a desperation for freedom, a terror at the thought of coming out of their hiding place — these are all expressions I've received. What you receive will be unique to you.

So long as your intentions are being expressed from a visceral connection to your need to heal within you, they're all valid and useful. As you become aware of these messages bubbling up to the surface, keeping notes in a journal can be helpful. It's frustrating to have a great moment of clarity around the needed intentions only to have it fade from memory soon after. Having these experiences written down can help you easily refresh your connection to the felt sense of that intention whenever you need to.

How to Get Started

Getting started with feeling inward can be tricky, as it's easy to second-guess anything you think you are sensing, to overthink it, to doubt what you feel, etc. Luckily for anyone who is called to this intensive kind of healing work, a great place to start is simply with the felt sense of that calling to heal.

Feel in your body where you can sense that drive, that demand to heal coming from. What does it feel like? Even if you can't at first put words to it, you can pay attention to what it feels like to you. A perfect intention could be something like: *I feel this desperate call to heal from deep inside of me. I am dedicated to doing whatever I need to in order to enable that to happen.* Use the words that resonate with your own calling. Keep it simple and honest and let that carry you into your first sessions. As you explore, grow, and become more self-aware, you'll develop the skills and discernment to listen to yourself and trust what you hear.

The Master Intention

To be effective with medicine work, you need to have a general idea of where you are ultimately trying to go. The light at the end of the medicine work tunnel is you feeling complete with your healing work, whatever that means for you, even if you don't fully know what that would look like just yet. This is your *master intention*.

Mine is to feel whole and fully alive. That is my North Star, and it has guided me again and again in all of my healing efforts whenever I have reached inward for my next intentions. It has profoundly reshaped the course of my life.

Having this clear master intention for the work is crucial because otherwise the process can easily become like a dog that keeps chasing every squirrel that flicks its tail in their direction, with the chasing becoming the point. It's the whole spiritual seekers versus finders thing. You are called in a general direction and overcome any challenges, pass through any gateways, you need to in order to get there. You can't possibly know what twists or turns will be on the path ahead, but you need to be clear on the direction that you are trying to go, or you can aimlessly wander around in your inner world forever.

Releasing control and permitting yourself to fall towards that light at the end of the tunnel is how you enable your psyche, your body, to heal itself layer by layer. It's how you enable medicine work to do its work.

So long as you are in the process of healing and feeling more and more integrated and whole, then your objectives are being met beautifully. Allow yourself to evolve into your authentic nature, even if you don't consciously yet know what that might be. I've often found myself surprised and delighted by how this true healing and growth ripples throughout my experience of life. I've never once found any of those changes to diminish my life in any way.

CHAPTER 12

SET AND SETTING

"Set and Setting" is an old-school term that refers to the importance of the mindset you take into a psychedelic experience and the setting in which you do it, including the people around you. Go into a recreational or expansive experience with a lot of fear and anxiety and you may be in for a bumpy, difficult ride. Do those same psychedelics around people you don't trust, or in a location where you don't feel safe, and you can easily find yourself in bad trip territory. As you can probably imagine, for medicine work, your mindset and the setting are even more important.

The Setting

The setting for your medicine work must above all feel safe. It must also feel thoughtfully prepared, comfortable, and private. This is the container for your medicine work, and your felt sense of its integrity is a vital part of the overall experience.

Privacy

In medicine work, you absolutely must feel safe and free to make whatever sounds you need to make and say whatever you need to say. If you don't feel comfortable to scream or shout profanities, or if you feel that the things you say could be overheard by someone outside of the container, you'll almost certainly hold back, consciously, or not, in what you are willing or able to express.

I was once in the process of medicine work in a space where the guide opened a window to help cool down the room. Immediately I came out of the deep, energetic flow to focus on concerns about who outside might hear me. The safe container for our work had been ruptured, and I no longer felt like I was in a private space where I felt safe to express anything that needed to be.

Many who grew up in violent or unpredictable homes develop highly sensitive antennas for how others are responding to them. It was a matter of survival. For me, this created a seemingly telepathic ability to monitor those in my environment for even the most subtle shift in mood.

Although I had built the confidence to be free with my guide in our sessions, having the window open made me instantly cautious to not attract unwanted attention. I felt a deep, instinctive need coming from the wounded place trying to heal, urging me to close off my expression to account for not knowing who might hear me and how they might react to it. I no longer felt safe.

When dealing with the healing of trauma, having confidence in the absolute privacy and confidentiality of your process is crucial. Yes, people do healing work in groups too. There you are choosing and accepting who can witness your expression, and many in groups do not seem to fully let go into the process anyway. In private sessions, knowing that others can potentially observe your process through an open window, or through a wall, or from the next room, will almost certainly cause you to withhold, consciously or not, from free expression. Feeling safe that your expressions are private is essential to enabling yourself to be truly open and vulnerable.

Room to Move Freely
To do real medicine work, you also need a large, safe space where you can move and thrash around should you need to. I've always worked on

a large, thick, supportive mat (queen-mattress size or larger) on the floor with plenty of room around me. I've never gotten up and run amok in the room, but certainly others have. The container *must* permit freedom of movement, and the room has to be free of potentially dangerous things to run into or fall on. Lying on a sofa with headphones on just won't cut it — such a setting brings too much self-regulation into play and hampers the free flow of emotional release.

Music

Music is a remarkable tool for helping to shape the experience of a medicine work journey. I've had a wide variety of musical experiences help guide my sessions. Normally your guide will choose the music and change it throughout the session based on what is required. It's a powerful tool to help guide emotion.

In sessions with MDMA, the music is usually peaceful and soothing. Gentle and calm music can help create a sense of safety and set a pace that helps it all feel manageable. Whereas more intense music will create a more challenging journey, and sometimes this is actually desired. I found it helpful while on mushrooms to have the music change throughout the session: soothing during the launch, more intense during and around the peak, inspirational during the comedown, and back to peaceful again as I rested and came back to the present time and place.

I recommend minimizing contemporary or mainstream music. Sometimes familiar music can be used as a potent trigger to help access wounded areas. But most often you'll want to stay away from what you'd normally listen to because it can take you out of your deep state and into the everyday state of mind that you normally listen to that music in. My experience has been that music with lyrics can be really distracting and can pull you out of any real depth to float on the surface while listening to the words. It always seems to take something away from the session when someone else is talking (or singing) the whole time.

Some guides or therapists have the client wear headphones for listening to the music. Sometimes this is because the location, such as a therapist's office, can't have loud music, or it can be distracting for their office neighbors. Again, this is a poor choice of location for psychedelic healing work because if you can't play loud music, you also can't yell or scream should you feel that you need to. Headphones are also easily dislodged if you start moving around, causing a further distraction to pull you out of the flow of the work.

It's far better to be in a location where you can have music playing at a helpful volume in the container where you are working. I've found that music needs to be fairly loud as it helps in the effort to get you out of your head and just feel whatever your body is expressing. It shouldn't be so loud you can't talk to or hear your guide, but you want to be able to feel it.

In my sessions, my guide will often vary the volume based on what I'm experiencing. If I'm deep in physical catharsis with a lot of movement or purging, the louder the better. If I'm in a more peaceful space, and expressing verbally, then making the music a bit quieter so my guide can interact with me tends to feel much more helpful.

Recording

Some people want to make a video or audio recording of their sessions. I've always felt that this was a terrible idea. A recorder is like a third person in the room and will change the dynamic and affect the potential of what can happen in the session. Anything digital can be replicated or get into the wrong hands too easily. What would it feel like to have such intimate and vulnerable experiences, something that someone who hasn't been through it could never understand, made public?

If you are set on recording your journey in any way, first ensure your guide is okay with it. They may not be comfortable having themselves documented doing this sensitive work. If you do decide to record the session, do the recording yourself. Use your own video or audio recorder and do not let anyone else handle the recorded files. Never let someone else do the recording and then email or otherwise digitally send them to you. Digital files are too easy to lose control of.

I've heard of guides making recordings without the participant's knowledge, even offering them for sale after the session. Always directly ask your guides if they make any form of recordings and be clear that you do not want to be recorded in any way during the session without your explicit consent. I do not believe that this is a widespread issue, but forewarned is forearmed. It's easier to ask ahead of time than to ensure that all copies and backups of a digital recording have been deleted once they're already made.

The only records made from my own medicine work have been handwritten session notes. My first guide would make these notes and then give them to me at the end of the day. Later, I started keeping my own journals and asked my guides to make the notes in there. I find it helpful to go back and review them later, during my integration process. It's also incredible to go back a year or more and see so clearly how far I've come with the work.

Tools

Don't be afraid to experiment in your sessions with tools. I've tried a wide variety of tools and props to help the energy to move in medicine work sessions and I use many of them regularly. It's all about finding what works for you. I've learned to trust my instincts to an incredible degree. If an idea occurs to me in everyday life for something that might be helpful in a session, you can bet that I'll be giving it a try soon.

These are some of the tools that I use regularly in psychedelic work:

- **Mementos**
  Meaningful photos or other objects from your life that bring up memories related to your intentions for the work can be really helpful. Many times, I've had photos lined up in the medicine work space where I could see them throughout the day. I've also brought objects with me, like one of my grandfather's old cowboy hats. Memory triggers that can help keep you focused on where the healing is trying to happen can have a potent effect on the work that you do that day.

- **Eye masks**

  Eye masks are an essential tool for psychedelic healing work. They shut out visual distractions and help focus your attention inward to feel the subtle nuances of emotion. They can also be challenging at times too because using them can add greatly to the intensity of everything you are feeling. When the feelings coming through are about as subtle as a pack of grizzly bears with chainsaws, the mask is completely optional. Don't be afraid to go without it. There is no right or wrong and you should always go with what feels right to you.

- **Sketchbook**

  I've found sketching to be a helpful additional way to express myself. I keep a large sketchbook and a pack of colored pencils next to the mat with every session. If I'm going to use them, it's normally as the medicines are settling in or as I'm coming down from them. During the actual journey, it can be hard to see well enough to sketch, and hard to sit still. But the urge to sketch has come up during some sessions and was a helpful tool at those times too.

  Sometimes, though this is rare, I want to write something down or express myself in written words during a session. My journal is too small for me to see or write in during a session, so I write large on my sketch pad. It can be hard to read it later, but I usually sort out what I was trying to say.

- **Surrogates**

  There are times in medicine work where I've found it hard to stay in the objective observer mode and hold a loving space for the younger me doing the expressing. This is where a surrogate, like a teddy bear, can be really useful. I always have mine on the mat with me for every session. Instinctively I know when to grab him during the work. I usually don't even know I've done it. But I'll find myself hugging him gently and speaking the assurances I otherwise would say to that fearful younger aspect of me trying to heal.

To be clear, there is absolutely a time for those wounded aspects to blend into you completely, to become you. There are also times when the objective observer and the aspect of you expressing are distinctly different. There tends to be an ebb and flow, and neither integration nor separation should be rejected or thought of as wrong. Most of the healing seems to happen with the objective observer holding a safe space for the emotions being expressed — it's less overwhelming for the part that is in the healing process. The surrogate stuffed animal, pillow, or whatever it is for you, can make staying in the observer mode much easier when things get intense.

- **Mirrors**

A large hand mirror has proven invaluable countless times in sessions. I ensure that it has a plastic surface so that it can't pose a safety hazard should I accidentally break it. There have been many times where I've felt stuck and instinctively grabbed the mirror to start a conversation with myself and talk out whatever was feeling stuck. It works really, really well.

I remember fondly one time when I was using the mirror to express to that younger me that what happened to him wasn't his fault. Looking him (me) right in the eyes, I said it over and over again, and could see him listening and considering this new point of view. I then spontaneously looked at my guide and said, *Good Will Hunting!* She immediately realized I was referring to that movie's famous scene where the therapist (played by Robin Williams) tells Will that the abuse he'd suffered wasn't his fault. He says it several times to get it to sink in for Will. We both cracked up for a truly beautiful moment and then I dropped right back into doing the work. My sense of humor spontaneously manifests in sessions like this all of the time; it, too, is a powerful tool for healing. I never try to be funny or to plan it, it just happens authentically and adds a bit of needed relief to deeply intensive work.

- **Other tools**

Other tools I find helpful are:

- **Percussion-style massage gun.** This is a gun-shaped handheld massager with a small padded ball on the end that has a hammering action. It's normally used by athletes and physical therapists for working out tight muscles. I use it on my abdomen, sides, and hips when I'm feeling stuck. My guide has used it on my back for the same reason. It's worked well and many times has gotten me through a roadblock to enable me to keep going deeper into the work.
- **Plastic Wiffle bats.** These are for beating the hell out of a pillow when anger or frustration needs help moving.
- **Weighted blankets.** These give a sense of safety and being grounded. I've had these blankets be a real game changer when a lot of fear was coming up. I've also had them feel claustrophobic and needed to kick them off quickly to not have panic escalate and dominate the journey.
- **Yoga straps.** These are long woven straps that are used to help with stretching. I can use these to help stretch out my legs, hips, and sides during a session, and many times a flurry of words or emotions have come pouring out as I do.

Mindset

The mindset you take into a medicine work session has nearly complete control over how that experience will go and what you will gain from it. Beyond your intentions for the work, there are some key concepts to integrate and embody that will help you get the most benefit.

You Aren't Trying to Get Rid of Anything

Medicine work is a compassionate, holistic healing process. This is why one of the most fundamental concepts to ensure that you are on board with, is that you aren't trying to get rid of anything within yourself. There are not blocks of good and bad things that can be removed or altered independent of everything else: *It's all interconnected webs of the meaning that make up your perspective on life in there.* This includes your emotional wounds and the defenses that protect them, which are often the cause of the problematic behaviors and feelings that affect one's experience of life so profoundly.

Even the old, stagnant emotional energy that is released through catharsis isn't being gotten rid of — instead, its natural free-flowing state is being restored. When these aspects of your psyche are vilified, it creates a tension that only strengthens and intensifies them. Resisting and trying to get rid of them only pulls the knot tighter and moves you further away from any progress in your healing efforts.

Surrender

Surrender is what enables medicine work to work. It's when you give up struggling to keep everything the same out of a misguided sense that this will keep you safe, and you release any effort to control or manage how your intentions to heal are carried out. Ultimately, surrender is fully allowing the experience to manifest and flow through you in whatever way it needs to.

Sometimes a person (like yours truly) has to have a medicine journey on a larger dose to get past their hardwired, full-time habitual need to have control over everything. At other times in medicine work, even small doses can help facilitate a deep opening.

Many years ago, when I was in AFF (accelerated free fall) skydiving training, I would be incredibly frightened before and during the flight to jump altitude. My mind would be spinning with thoughts of backing out and riding the plane back down to land. I would go through one rationalization after another about why it was okay to change my mind and not go through with it. But a deeper part of me wanted the beautiful, liberating experience of the free fall and then the peaceful soaring canopy ride to the ground, and it was my intention to have that experience. I was really anxious about it, but also determined to do it.

When it was my turn to jump, I would work myself to the doorway and when it was time, I'd roll forward and out into the open sky. Without fail, every single time, the millisecond I was no longer in contact with the airplane, my fear evaporated and turned into excitement as my mind surrendered any thought of control and I was simply in the experience of it. I felt pure exhilaration, and strangely, a deep sense of peace as I rocketed at terminal velocity towards the ground. I've known others who would try skydiving and stay tense and terrified all the way down; they never surrendered and ended up resisting the experience until well after they had landed safely.

The majority of my medicine work journeys have gone the same way as my skydiving experiences. I've been so scared before the start that I would be physically shaking and feeling nauseous. My mind would be working overtime looking for a good reason to back out and leave. Even with medicines I knew would not have a big fear component, like MDMA, the fear of the upcoming release of control and opening of powerful emotions had terror bubbling up from the deep places within. As soon as the medicines were ingested and there was no going back, I would always experience a deep relaxation within me, a surrender to the experience.

Trust and Vulnerability

Historically, I'm not someone who would ever let myself be vulnerable, especially when anxious or fearful. But when I do medicine work, I allow the weakest, most fearful parts of myself to come forward and be vulnerable, because it is their time to be heard and to heal. I'm deeply trusting that the medicine work process is absolutely and without exception in my best interest and moving my experience of life in a positive and rewarding direction, even when I otherwise feel scared about the upcoming work.

When you come into medicine work from a heavily defended position, your previously stated intentions to heal can easily be overridden by the intentions from those defenses that seek to protect you from feeling too much. The willingness to trust in the process and permit yourself to be vulnerable in medicine work comes from the same place that your determination to heal does. You can't think your way to it, you have to feel inwardly for it and allow it to come forward.

Handling Challenges

Medicine journeys can at times be challenging, but they should never feel punishing. Moments of feeling overwhelmed are normal and fine. Deep breaths and surrendering into the process can allow difficult feelings to flow right through you. But if the challenge feels like it's stuck and it continues unresolved for too long, something needs to change in the session. A qualified guide will be in tune with this and will know how to help, so it's important to speak up and ask for help. It's what a guide is there for.

So many of us desperately wanted and needed help when our traumas were created but didn't get it. Asking for help and actually receiving it can be a profound corrective experience. Your guide is there for you, so you don't have to go through any of this alone this time around. This is why having a truly qualified guide and the mindset that it's safe to ask for and accept help when you need it is so important.

Many times, I would hit this point and my medicine guide would spring into action, massaging the vagal nerves on the sides of my neck and reminding me to breathe. Sometimes she would ask me to open my eyes and look around the room for a moment, bringing me into the present moment so my body could relax. Other times I would hear a tuning fork being struck and touched to the bottoms of my feet and the palms of my hands, bringing me back into my body in the here and now.

Sometimes the type of music was changed, or the volume dramatically reduced so my mind and body could calm down. Sometimes the guide would burn some palo santo, which my mind would notice, and I would be pulled out of the downward spiraling loop of fear and resistance.

Sometimes the intervention has been simple touch, holding my hand or putting a hand on my chest or back. Physical connection like this has grounded me and brought me back to the present moment in my mind and body, again and again.

Regardless of whether you are deep breathing, surrendering and handling significant challenges by yourself, or asking for help from your guide, nothing in a session is too big to be handled with the proper mindset. The key is to shift from the perspective of being lost in a storm, tumbling in the waves, and being pounded on the rocks, to one of being the sea itself, containing it all and never threatened in the least by it.

You May Not Remember Everything

It's common to not have clear memories of everything that you say, think, or do during a medicine work session. This is normal and should be accepted going into the experience. Having these memories to review and intellectualize later doesn't necessarily help the healing process — in fact, it can lead to the creation of a *bypass*, in which we grab on to ideas or concepts in order to avoid feeling the underlying feelings.

You'll likely remember chunks of the day, and many times during your integration you'll find various memories will come bubbling up. That old cliché about the journey being more important than the destination is remarkably apt when discussing medicine work. The healing comes mostly from having gone through the process, and much less from what you think or remember about it later.

Hold It Lightly

It can be seductive to seek out those *aha!* moments, those profound insights that can come so easily in psychedelic experiences. They feel great, and they make it seem like something important is happening, that progress is being made.

When you go into a medicine work session with the intention of finding "the answers" or seeking epiphanies or recovering specific memories, it can encourage you to stay up in your head. This can easily derail any deep unwinding in the medicine work that is trying to happen.

Then, when insights do eventually come bursting through, the mind can want to start playing with its shiny new toy, turning the insight this way and that to extract the most sense of fulfillment and importance from the experience. It can be tempting to start looking for meaning and connections based on whatever insights have come up for you. When you are high on psychedelics, meaning can get intensified and at times skewed. It can easily become a bypass, a way of avoiding the deep emotional work you came to the session for. My guide's sage advice was always to *hold it lightly* and not fixate on it. If it's important, it'll still be important later.

A trick that I've learned is that if during a journey I find myself heavily focused on or fearful of losing a particular insight or idea, I ask my guide to write it down for me. Once I know that I can go back to it at any time, I find that my mind is much more willing to relax around it.

Your Guide Is Only Human

A guide is only human. No matter how well trained or experienced they are, they can never truly and completely know what is going on for you in a session. They might have a really good idea about it through communication, intuition, empathy, and experience. But while for you the universe is seeming to come apart at the molecular level and emotions are surging through you in ecstatic or terrifying ways, they just see someone lying on the floor with an eye mask on.

Or maybe you are having body movements, or are making sounds, talking, purging, or whatever. They can see the ways that emotional energy is expressing itself through you, but they may not always have the same idea about the context of it that you do.

This is why communication before, during (when possible), and after is critical. It gives the guide a chance to learn about you and your experiences. This helps shape how they hold a space for you. And it helps you to build trust that they can hold this non-judgmental space to keep you safe, so you can feel safe to express deeper emotional material.

Ultimately, guides are there to bear witness to your healing process with compassion and without tainting it with their own triggers, insecurities, judgments, or assumptions. They are there to hear what needs to be heard or see what needs to be seen and to offer loving compassion for whatever needs to present itself, no matter what it might be, and without exception.

Sometimes a guide may misread what you've shared or expressed and reflect your experience back to you inaccurately. In such cases it's easy, especially if you are still affected by the medicine, to feel unseen or unheard. It can hurt after being so vulnerable. At these times it's key to be open about both your experience of not feeling seen as well as what you feel was going on for you in the scenario that the guide misread.

A good guide will always be open to this kind of feedback, and when received with openness and kindness, it will make your connection that much stronger. Instead of closing off from hurt, lean into the vulnerability, and allow yourself a corrective experience.

CHAPTER 13

AGREEMENTS

Clear agreements between yourself and your guide about the medicine work process are another important part of shaping your mindset and sense of trust for the upcoming journey. The following agreements and any others you think of should be reviewed and accepted before each and every session.

Safety

You commit to the safety of yourself, your guide, and the space that you are working in. The agreement is that you can express anything that you need to, but that it will never be acted out as violence or aggression towards yourself, your guide, anyone else, or in the destruction of the space in which the journey is being held.

If you feel the need to physically vent anger or frustration, then your guide can set you up with a pile of pillows to pound on. No matter how enraged I feel or how otherwise out of my mind I might be on the psychedelics, I'm always clear on where the lines are between appropriate and inappropriate behavior, just as I'm always clear on what is safe and what isn't for me and for my guide.

Sex

Both you and your guide commit that no sexual contact of any kind will happen during the session. Huge feelings can be released, as can BIG sexual energy. This can at times get projected on the guide with an intensity that feels real and urgent. This is especially true with empathogens like MDMA, 3-MMC, and 2C-B.

Any well-trained guide knows that this is possible and that although any feeling you need to express in a session is absolutely fine, he or she would never meet that energy or reciprocate. I know of guides who have violated this principle, who have violated the trust placed in them by their clients and exploited their vulnerability. **A guide who violates this agreement under any circumstance is committing sexual assault, a crime against someone with no capacity to give consent. No exceptions.**

This agreement is a commitment on your part, just as much as it is for the guide. Absolutely anything you feel during a journey is valid and worthy of expression. But you do not have any right to become sexually aggressive or to make any kind of sexual contact with your guide, no matter what you might be feeling or how you imagine them to feel in response. Even heavily under the influence of psychedelics, you are absolutely able to understand and honor this agreement at all times.

Staying Put

You commit that you will not leave the session space before you are completely sober and both you and your guide feel it is safe for you to leave. You are always free to shift from medicine work to a peaceful, expansive experience with your guide as you wait for the drugs to wear off, if that is what feels right to you. The music can stop, and you can move from lying on the floor to sitting in a comfy chair. **But you should never leave the premises before you are fully sober, whether you are driving or not.** It's a matter of physical and psychological safety.

Navigating the outside world and other people while you are still high from the medicines, especially after having been deep within yourself, could cause intense psychological distress and leave you vulnerable and easily taken advantage of. And you could find those deep emotions that started to move in the session rushing to the surface when you have no support and little, if any, ability to manage them. Having a bad trip in public, or alone at home, would be traumatizing and could even cause you to be a danger to yourself or others.

Confidentiality

Your guide commits that they will keep any and all details about your medicine work experience confidential and will not share them under any circumstances unless they believe that you pose a true threat to yourself or someone else.

You commit that you'll keep your guide's participation in this work confidential and will not publicly share details about them in any way.

A Cooling-Off Period

You commit that you'll not act on any important decisions based on anything that comes up in a session for at least a few weeks to a month unless it's an imminent safety issue. Proposing marriage, breaking up, seeking divorce, moving out, quitting your job, telling off your boss — these all can seem like exactly what you need to do, and it can sometimes feel like you need to do it RIGHT NOW.

But after a few weeks, when everything has had time to settle, a major life change might not seem like such a great idea any more. With some time, you might feel that more subtle changes are needed, or none at all. Or, after a few weeks, you might still be clear that this big change is warranted.

The point is that you always want to give yourself a cooling-off period after a session, before you do or say something you can't take back that would have a big impact on yours or someone else's life. My experience has been that the more urgently I feel the need to act based on something that came up in a journey, the more important it is that I give myself some time to process it.

Boundaries

You and your guide commit that your boundaries will be honored and respected.

Setting and honoring personal boundaries in medicine work are vital parts of the integrity of the process, as with the previous points about sexual contact, aggression, and violence. The commitment is a two-way street, where you and your guide are establishing clear boundaries to be honored for each other.

Other boundaries exist that may need to be established during the process of the work. If you were previously okay with your guide doing bodywork on you, but now would prefer not to, that is your right, and it should be honored when you clearly ask to not be touched at this time.

Or, if your guide is talking a bit more than feels good to you at the moment, it's okay to ask him or her to stop. In that situation I might say, *I feel like I need a bit of space right now.* Or, *I don't feel like talking right now.* Those requests should be honored with no preference about it coming back from the guide. They are there to support you with what you need.

On one journey I hit a point of intense fear that I wasn't getting to release and open for me. The music was loud and felt overwhelming, which was causing my defenses to lock down even harder, like a knot being pulled tighter and tighter.

I asked my guide to please turn it down, and he turned it down just slightly. I know that he was thinking that I needed the music loud to help me to break through whatever I was feeling and that I only needed to surrender to it. Having the music loud had helped me in this way many times before.

But this was different, and I was having difficulty convincing him of that. The point being — I shouldn't have had to convince him of anything. I felt rage building in me at being forced to endure something that was not only unhelpful, but actively interfering with my medicine work process. I ended up walking out of the room to sit away from the music so I could collect myself and hopefully get back to doing real work. He meant well, of that I'm absolutely certain. But this was a screw-up by a guide who was normally in tune with me.

Nobody in a medicine work session should ever be forced to endure something that they are being clear is not working for them. I'd verbally set a boundary and it was ignored, which affected my ability to trust him in the future.

What he should have done was see that I was in distress, that the current approach wasn't working in that moment, and turned the music off for a little while. From there we could have helped my nervous system to calm down, to get my body out of the fight, flight, or freeze mode, and the work could likely have continued.

Instead, I spent the rest of the day not trusting that I could be vulnerable with him. I no longer trusted that I wasn't going to be forced into doing or enduring things that did not feel good or right for me. I didn't get any more meaningful inner work done that day, and it ended up being a frustrating waste of the considerable time, energy, and money that I'd spent to be there.

Another guide put a lot of pressure on me to follow his protocol of wearing an eye mask while working with psilocybin mushrooms. This really interfered with the work because what I was feeling was way too intense for that. I was genuinely terrified. Instead of following my instincts, setting clear boundaries, and refusing to wear the eye mask, I suffered through it instead.

Normally, in a guided medicine journey on mushrooms, eye masks are a potent tool to help you to focus inward on the waves of feeling flowing through you. It is a way to work deeply and be in touch with subtle emotional energies. But when someone is working through trauma, as I clearly was, requiring an eye mask is contraindicated and ill-advised. A mask must always be optional.

I kept struggling with the idea that I would disappoint or frustrate him if I took the mask off, that I would be doing the medicine work wrong, even though wearing it felt wrong and counterproductive. These experiences instilled a potent fear in me around using mushrooms for healing at all. This took a long time for me to overcome, which was a shame because mushrooms work like nothing else in the way that they can help with inner exploration and healing.

Often trauma victims were alone and helpless in their feelings during the circumstances that caused their trauma. The felt isolation of the eye masks as those feelings are brought up again can be overwhelming and even debilitating, not productive. My defenses would frequently lock down even harder, and those medicine work sessions ended up feeling more punishing than productive.

After that I always set clear boundaries with my guides that I would only work with an eye mask when it felt right for me. I trusted myself to know when it would be helpful and when it would be too much. In some sessions I would go back and forth putting it on and taking it off many times. I put an eye mask on when I felt scattered or disconnected and would take it off if I found myself overwhelmed and unable to get past it.

We use guides to help us focus and go deeper, and it's their job to help us find our way inwards. But always honor your instincts and your own truth, even if they are in conflict with what your guide wants or says. A qualified and experienced guide will always honor any clearly expressed boundaries.

CHAPTER 14

PREPARING FOR A MEDICINE WORK JOURNEY

We've previously discussed how you can help prepare yourself for medicine work in general. Here, we'll talk about getting ready for an actual medicine work session and the integration period after. To get the most from the medicine work, it's crucial to begin preparing yourself ahead of time physically, emotionally, mentally, and socially.

Putting in the best effort that you can ahead of time is an important part of your commitment to your healing process and will help maximize the enduring benefits you can receive from the journey.

The Process of Preparation

One Month Before
The month leading up to a medicine work session is a great time to begin preparing your mind, body, and life for the upcoming healing process.

Medicine work can at times be physically taxing, and I often have a sense of intense fatigue after sessions that can sometimes last for a few days. Regular exercise and stretching in the weeks leading up to it can help prepare your body for the upcoming work. So can taking care of yourself with nutritious food, minimal or no alcohol, and minimal caffeine.

Recreational drugs should *never* be used in the month before a session. They affect the neurotransmitters that the medicines need to work. Coming into a session depleted can significantly degrade the experience and can potentially introduce serious side effects.

It's usually recommended that you stop any unnecessary medicines or supplements weeks, or at least several days, before a psychedelic journey, if it can be done so safely. **You and your guide must carefully review any prescribed drugs or supplements that you cannot stop before the session, and both of you need to confirm that they will not have potentially dangerous interactions with the psychedelics that you will be taking.** For example, some antidepressants can be fatal if mixed with MDMA, and ketamine can be fatal if mixed with alcohol, opioids, or tranquilizers.

Getting good, deep sleep is crucial as it dramatically affects both mood and clarity of thought. It's also good to have a practice for centering yourself and relaxing throughout your day. This could be meditation, mindful activities like walks, playing music, or other hobbies that foster a sense of joy, peace, and ease. The whole idea is to keep pulling yourself back to a calm, relaxed, and open state as often as you can.

Through this time, it is ideal to be working regularly with your psychological support person. Working with them, and your medicine guide, can help you to get clear within yourself on the felt sense of your intentions.

It's also really helpful to prepare your social and family life for the integration period by letting those close to you know what you are doing and that in the days or weeks after you might be emotionally processing a lot, which could cause your mood to swing around unpredictably. Knowing this ahead of time can help prevent your integration process from causing needless offense, confusion and conflict with those around you and can hopefully prepare them to meet you with compassion, patience and understanding.

The Day Before
The day before a medicine work session is actually the start of the session. It's when you begin shifting from your everyday life into a new mode in

which you are open, ready, and willing to deeply heal. This is a day where you can celebrate all of you, showing even those parts of you in the darkest corners of your being some love and compassion.

As I stated before, it is really important to avoid any alcohol, recreational drugs, and unnecessary prescriptions or supplements. Keep caffeine and nicotine minimal or avoid them altogether. Eating healthy foods and getting plenty of calories can help to carry you through the next day. And it's important to stay really well hydrated.

If you can, get easy exercise like a long walk, a bike ride, yoga, or whatever you enjoy. This can be really helpful for managing any anxiety you might be feeling. I highly recommend gentle stretching as it helps open your body for the flow of emotional energy. I especially like to do stretches that open the chest, abdomen, hips, and sides.

This is the time to really start settling into the medicine work mindset, allowing your defenses to relax and those vulnerable, wounded parts to begin feeling safe to be more open. This is also the time to revisit your intention for the work, reconnecting to the visceral felt sense of it, feeling deeply and listening carefully for anything trying to express. The point is to begin allowing it to come forward, to begin the expression process to whatever degree it is ready to.

I always find it really beneficial to spend this day in quiet, mindful reflection. As much as I can, I avoid stimulating activities, normal life drama, TV, music, work, crowds, other people's anxieties. I'll often write in my journal, exploring my intentions as well as any questions or concerns. I'll also write down any ideas, questions or concerns that I want to go over with my guide as well.

The Day Of

On the day of a session, it's usually recommended that you be fasting, if it is safe for you to do so. This has a direct effect on the timing and potency of the ingested medicines. It's also a matter of safety, should you happen to vomit during the work. Some guides will recommend fasting for at least four hours before taking the medicines. I always go into the experience having fasted since the night before. My experience has always been that once I'm in the medicine work, hunger is no longer an issue. And, it's good to be well hydrated when you come into your session.

For addicts like myself, caffeine can be tricky. Going completely without always leads to me getting a piercing headache late that night, like a hot nail between the eyes. And having any after a session will guarantee that my sleep will be disturbed that night. So, I'll have a small cup of weak tea without any additives several hours before, as soon as I wake up that morning. This holds me over until the next day without the truly horrendous headache that would otherwise come. Too much caffeine can have a noticeable negative effect on the journey, introducing a level of anxiety that makes it much more difficult to feel safe to be open. But my experience is that just a little bit seems to forestall the headache without having a perceptible influence on the work.

The same is true for nicotine. Skip it if you possibly can the day of the session, as it can have a noticeable effect on the medicine work. I know that you'll likely be nervous, and a smoke would seem to help. But remember, that anxiety can be your first gateway down into the rabbit hole. The point isn't to escape this anxiety, but to use it to help the process of going inwards.

Before every session I get some light exercise, such as taking a walk, and I do light stretching. The intention here is to help open sensation and the flow of energy through the body.

I recommend wearing loose-fitting clothing that lets you feel comfortable both lying down and moving around, should you need to. And you'll likely want to avoid wearing jewelry or scented products like lotions, perfumes, or colognes — all of which can create unwanted distractions. It's a good idea to check with your guide to see if there is anything else that they'd like for you to bring with you or that you should avoid bringing.

Last, it's important to stay mindful of your thoughts and feelings. It can be easy to get swept away in fearful fantasies and worry. When this happens, the key is to gently bring yourself back to the present moment, back to your breath, and own that you are feeling anxious about the upcoming session. This is when it's important to refocus on the felt sense of your intentions for the medicine work as well as reconnect with your deep drive to heal.

CHAPTER 15

THE MEDICINE WORK JOURNEY

The Big Day

The big day is finally here! It's time for a medicine work journey. Whether you've used psychedelics recreationally or expansively before or not, properly supported and with your intentions from deep within guiding the way, this will almost certainly be a new and life-changing experience for you.

Fear

Feeling anxiety or fear before medicine work is normal, and it's important to honor that as a vital part of the process. It's not something to try to escape or get rid of, but the instinctive urge to do so can be overwhelming. Resisting the discomfort of the feeling of fear pushes you away from the underlying wounds you are trying to heal. Some might dissociate and feel numb or indifferent instead. Anything you feel going into medicine work is valid and normal. The key is to allow whatever is authentically expressing from within you to be there. Talk with your guide about it, and be open and honest about your experience.

I've had many moments before medicine work sessions when my courage has felt like it might fail me, as nearly overwhelming fear had me right on the edge of running away. Countless times I've had the inner dialogue of *I don't have to do this if I don't want to; I can leave before this starts if I want to.*

In those moments it was reconnecting to my intentions for healing and bringing myself back into the present moment that saved the day. I let those feelings of fear and doubt exist simultaneously with the felt sense of my underlying intention and determination to do the work. Where before I was only feeling the fear, connecting with my intention invoked a sense of empowerment and strength to do what needs to be done. I was able to *allow* the fear, which made me an observer of it in the present moment. And, of course, I did all of this while taking deep, calming breaths. All is welcome, all is manageable when I don't resist it. Breathe and allow.

The Experience

Ceremony

Having an established ritual or ceremony is a great way to get centered and focused for the upcoming work while getting connected to the visceral felt-sense of your intentions. I'd like to think that Pavlov's dogs would agree that doing it the same way each time can help your body and mind drop into the medicine work space more easily.

For every medicine work session, my guide and I always get situated in the room, start the chosen music, then sit down on the mat facing each other to review both of our intentions and agreements for the day. Then we each "sage," wafting burning sage smoke over ourselves one at a time, with the intention that any stresses, distractions, or issues outside of this room are released and carried away on the smoke. Each session is closed with another round of sage, when I take time to express gratitude for the healing done that day, for the medicines, and for my guide.

I even have a specific T-shirt that I wear for every session. It has my slogan, *Find the next gate*, with some custom artwork I had made for me, of a person walking through a series of gateways, surrounded by the chemical symbols of the various psychedelic medicines I use. I only wear that shirt for medicine work, and when I put it on beforehand, my body starts physically responding and adjusting for the upcoming work. It's yet another layer of stating my intention to enable the healing process to happen.

There are many ways to develop your own rituals around medicine work. Some people have a special place, such as an altar, where the medicine is placed before the work begins. Some write their intentions on paper and burn them in a specific ornate bowl as a way of releasing control to that deeper wisdom within. Some say prayers, others do light yoga or stretching. Work with your guide and find what feels best to both of you.

Trust Fall

At the end of the opening ceremony, it's time to take the agreed upon psychedelic medicine(s). For me, this is always the point of no return, when I surrender to the healing process that continues to deepen as the medicines set in. The best way I can describe this is as a "trust fall."

The trust fall began as a team-building exercise: someone falls backwards from a standing position while keeping their body straight, trusting that the person standing behind them will catch them. They know that if they aren't caught, they'll hit the floor hard, since they aren't trying to protect themselves or control anything as they fall. But they do it anyway — thus, the trust.

In medicine work the trust fall is a deep surrender, trusting the healing process, your intrinsic wisdom, and your guide to always keep you safe and never give you more than you can handle. You roll out of the airplane door and go for the ride. There is only the quiet listening of a curious observer open to anything that wants or needs to express and the honest intention to allow it to do so.

In the Flow

Sometimes as the medicine is flowing through me, my body will start moving, making sounds, talking, laughing, crying, or any number of energetic releases all on its own. I just notice it happening and surrender to whatever needs to move and express.

At other times I can feel the need for something to express, but it feels too defended or too stuck to break free. In these circumstances, I'll proactively start doing what I feel is trying to happen. I never think about this, I just feel it and start doing it, experimenting to find what will uncork whatever is trying to express. I've learned to check any form of self-consciousness at the door when I start a medicine work session, so I have no concerns at all about how I might look or sound. Your guide has been there and knows what it's like to go through the process.

Guides have no interest in judging anything that is expressed in any way from you. They know that how trauma and pain is authentically expressed and released is completely unique to each individual. As you build trust in your guide and the healing process, you'll get more and more comfortable to just let it all go.

If it feels to me like movement wants to happen, I'll start moving my arms and legs or whatever feels right until my body takes over and it starts happening all by itself, kind of like turning the hand crank on one of those old-time cars. If I feel like something wants to be vocalized in words or sounds, I'll just start talking out loud or shouting or swearing, or whatever instinctively feels right, until it starts flowing authentically through me.

I'm not *trying* to do anything specific or come to any specific outcome. I'm just going with whatever feels like is trying to happen. Occasionally nothing comes of it, and I simply release it and go back to my breath.

I'll admit, it's a bizarre feeling. More than once, I've thought, *Holy shit, I can't believe this is real and is actually working!* But it's also empowering and inspiring to keep surrendering to see what and how much more is ready to express and heal.

This is where the tools you have available in a session can be helpful. A yoga strap to stretch with or a percussion massage gun to get sensation moving through my abdomen, back, or elsewhere on my body can start a flow of words or movement otherwise inaccessible. I'll gaze into my mirror to get the dialogue started and find what was trying to be said. Many times, I've grabbed my 5-MeO-DMT vape pens to permit a deeper energetic expression to happen.

I've learned to trust this process implicitly and completely. With every single medicine journey, I trust-fall into it, and the rest happens all by itself. I only get stuck or interrupt the process when I clamp down on it by resisting whatever it is trying to express, often fear or shame. When I do this, I have inadvertently locked the next gate that I need to pass through to go deeper.

Finding the Next Gate

Medicine work is the process of finding and passing through one gateway after another, each moving you deeper inwards. It's the expression of one emotional gateway that permits you to pass through to the next, exactly like in body-centered therapy. Admission to the next layer is never given until you unlock the current gateway by letting it express and release whatever it needs to. Layer by layer you work your way inwards towards the expression of the wound that has been asking to heal.

I've had a couple of journeys that didn't make it to the depth that was in my intention, but this is rare. Through experience I've learned that if I feel stalled or stuck in any way during the journey, that telling my guide what is happening and asking for help can get me right back on track. They help me come back to my body, back to my intentions, and back into the groove of the medicine work.

The Comedown

On psychedelics, the comedown is when you've passed the peak of the experience and the medicines are beginning to wear off. This is when your normal state of mind starts coming back online, including your usual ways of thinking and feeling.

It's normal to notice this as it's happening, and it can bring up its own feelings and challenges. Sometimes there can be a feeling of loss after having felt so open and free during the journey. At other times, there can be a sense of shame in having been so open, as frequently happened for me. And sometimes there is a sense of relief when the journey was a challenging one. I've certainly felt this at times too.

What is important to remember is that even though you are starting to come down from the high, you can still do a lot of great healing work. Listen and feel inward to see if anything more is asking to release, if anything from the day feels incomplete. If it does, share this with your guide. Sometimes speaking from that place within you will enable it to express. I've used many approaches, including talking/yelling/screaming, beating on a pillow, movement, etc. Other times I've used 5-MeO-DMT to get the stuck place to move, with the dosage chosen being based on what feels right to me and my guide in that moment.

If you otherwise feel complete with the day, the comedown is a great time to relax into your body and reflect on how the openness you felt in your mind and body during the journey was different from your everyday state. I do this so I can feel into and reestablish that openness again, to a degree, in my everyday life. It helps me to identify where I'm stuck or closed off much more easily.

It's important to continue holding whatever may have come up in the session lightly. This is the point where the mind can really start grinding away on those insights in an attempt to extract importance or meaning from them. When you lock down on the certainty of what, if anything, those insights mean for you, it diminishes the opportunity for a different point of view about it to come through. I've found that when my mind starts trying to create a narrative of what insights from a journey mean, it's often attempting to bypass the underlying emotional material that was expressing it in the first place. During the comedown, always do your best to come back to the present moment in your body when you find yourself processing in your head. Ask your guide for help if you need it.

I've also found that at times my mind will launch into obsessive thought loops or fantasies during the comedown. Especially with mushrooms, I'd find myself beating myself up with negative self-talk over and over and over again. I've learned that as soon as I notice any kind of loops starting, I'll ask my guide for help. They'll get me focused once more on my breathing while doing some body work to help my nervous system to calm down.

CHAPTER 16

INTEGRATION

The integration period after a medicine work session normally lasts a few weeks to a month. The first few days to a week are often the most challenging, with a variety of emotions and thoughts surging through in huge swells, though sometimes these days are joyful and easy instead.

Normally, it seems to be anxiety that causes the most difficulty in these first days after a session. Our minds don't cope well with faceless anxiety, so we can easily project it onto current situations or others around us. Or, as I've been told so many times, *Anxiety needs a home.* I've had to apologize for myself at times when the intensity of what I was feeling during my integration period has gotten away from me. The practice is to breathe and allow those feelings to flow and not resist them. Resisting builds pressure until something explodes, so do your best to simply let it flow and for a time try not to take the topics that anxiety creates so seriously.

Sure, you'll almost certainly see some changes ripple through your life over time, just for having done the medicine work. But the more mindful effort you put into the integration period, the more you can get out of it. It's common to feel incredible new freedoms from habitual thoughts, feelings, and behaviors immediately after medicine work, or any deep psychedelic experience. But it's also easy to begin slipping back into those old coping strategies in the days and weeks after. Some expansion and contraction is to be expected, as we've discussed before. But the longer you can mindfully stay present to the old ways of being and perceiving as well as the new freedoms, the more integrated those new paradigms can become. Our old habits are like deeply worn ruts on a dirt road. It takes focus and effort to help stay on the new path and not drift back into the ruts while creating your new default path of travel.

Support

Having proper emotional and psychological support for the integration period of your medicine work (and beyond) is essential. A lack of proper support can limit your gains or stall your growth altogether. In the midst of the wildly fluctuating states of mind and feelings that can occur after medicine work, it can be all too easy to lose perspective and get swept away by what you are feeling and thinking. Your support is there to help you to stay focused, gain clarity, and continue processing whatever emotional material is being expressed.

Ideally a therapist supporting medicine work will have had some significant experiences with psychedelics at some point in their lives. It is possible to do great work with a really good body-centered therapist who is open and accepting of medicine work. But those who have had deep psychedelic experiences have a different vibe. They sit differently in their own skin and will relate to you and your experience differently.

It may be difficult to find a therapist who has done deep medicine work. And those who have had big expansive experiences on psychedelics might not understand the difference between that and true medicine work. (Perhaps you could recommend a good book to them that takes great pains to explain the difference? ☺) But if they've at least had expansive psychedelic experiences that they believe were beneficial to them, then they can hold a space to talk through what is coming up for you.

It should be noted, though, that at this time there are therapists popping up that specifically offer "psychedelic integration" services.

Some of these seem to be hopping on the psychedelic bandwagon as a way to garner more clients. Of those that I've spoken to, few have any actual deep healing psychedelic experiences themselves. It's not clear what it is that makes them feel qualified to offer these services. I'm sure as time goes on that more genuinely experienced integration therapists will continue to become available.

Some medicine guides who are also licensed mental health professionals will make themselves available to be your source of support before and after each journey. If they are qualified to do this, then so much the better. I've worked this way before, and I found it to be beneficial. I didn't have to recount previous experiences as we were both already on the same page.

In addition to regular sessions with a qualified source of mental and emotional support, having family, friends, or a counselor who you can talk things through with can be helpful too. So long as they know to listen without interpreting, labeling, or judging whatever is coming up for you, talking it out can help keep the energy flowing through you. And, you simply cannot underestimate the power of a big hug or the power of compassionate touch when things feel really hard.

Self-Awareness

When you do medicine work, the biological and psychological systems that determine how you perceive, and thus feel, can be destabilized for days or even weeks afterwards. Depending on the medicines you used, you have likely temporarily depleted, or otherwise affected your body's ability to regulate, the neurochemicals that control your mood. You've also likely altered the structure, even the foundations, of that part of your psyche that shapes your felt sense of reality.

Because of this, as we discussed before, significant emotional disturbance is possible in the days following a big medicine work session. It's a normal and integral part of the process of growth. I often find this to be the most challenging part of medicine work. When you know to expect it and don't resist, things go much more smoothly, and it always passes. In fact, I view challenging integration periods as a sign of deep, positive work happening, so I welcome them with gratitude no matter how difficult I find it to be.

I've had moments of intense despair, frustration, anger, loneliness, grief, and even joy in the days following a big medicine journey. Sappy TV commercials have caused me to burst into tears. One time, as I sat on my sofa, my arms and legs started flailing around just like they had in the journey a few days before. I could have suppressed it if I'd been around other people, but since I was alone, I just relaxed as best I could and observed it with quiet curiosity and amazement.

I've also experienced strange new muscle tensions in my body — from subtle tightness to full-on spasms or cramps — as my defenses attempted to clamp down on the newly released emotional energy moving through me. This has been especially notable in my scalp, face, jaw, neck, and shoulders. I've also had it happen in my hips, low back, and abdomen.

When tension like this happens, massage, hot baths, heating pads, gentle stretching, or light exercise usually helps. I've also done solo ketamine work a couple of weeks after the medicine journey, explicitly focusing on breathing into those tense areas to get them to relax. In the ketamine space, I've found much more access to being able to will tight muscles to relax. I learn from this and can take some of that ability back into everyday life.

Staying self-aware and remembering to not take these feelings out of context, while also holding them lightly and not resisting them, has permitted them to flow through me naturally time and again. Remember that your integration period is an extension of the medicine work journey, and doing your best to permit whatever needs to be expressed to do so is just as important here as it was in the session.

Dueling Banjos

It's a strange sensation to feel two inner voices with different motivations, two drives really, acting simultaneously. This can happen in the integration period after big openings and releases. When previously suppressed aspects of your psyche are given freedom, the old habits that have always protected that part from being hurt or triggered might try suppressing it again. It's incredible to finally feel that locked-away part freely expressing itself and refusing to be hidden away any longer.

For example, a couple of days after a really big session, I was practicing piano. I could feel my most familiar state of mind, focused on progress and improvement, while I also felt a new sensation of joyfulness that included playfulness, curiosity, and delight. These two things felt separate inside of me. I felt a familiar concern rise over enjoying the piano too much and the reflex to stifle that pleasure before it could draw unwanted attention. But that new drive overrode it, insisting on being allowed to feel this joy, to have this fun and to take pride in doing something that seems really cool to me. It refused to be stuffed down and hidden away again. In session, it had gotten to breathe free air and it was not going to be forced completely back into hiding again. None of this was happening in words, only the feeling of emotional drives. One drive to stay open, the other to shut down. The words only come when I give verbal expression to those feelings.

A previously locked-away aspect of myself, the part that could experience enjoyment and express joy, was being given more energy to be an active part of my everyday life. Before, this capacity for joy was always clenched out of fear and drained of life to keep it stifled, because of a young boy's misconception that feeling joy would attract danger. Once that fear was deeply expressed and the reasoning behind it exposed, both the boy and the adult could see how untrue that actually was. Over time it started to become safe again to feel and express joy.

Eventually these two drives — to be open and to shut down — began blending into one as the perceived need for the defenses whose original job it was to protect me became perceived as less pressing. This was a direct experience of the process of becoming more integrated and feeling whole: aspects of my psyche that had previously been hidden away as a shadow were coming back home into the light.

Getting Discouraged

If you spend any amount of real time and effort in the medicine work healing process, you may have moments of doubt and despair. I've gone through it many times. This is when it's important to take a deep breath and reconnect with your drive and intentions to heal. This is where the truth about all of it lives: it's your anchor in any storm.

Once in a medicine work session I had shared with my medicine guide that I was feeling discouraged about some aspects of my growth that weren't progressing as I'd hoped. She looked at me and suggested that instead of saying to myself *I'm not* or *I can't*, that I should say, *I'm learning how to*.

Incredibly, this took all of the pressure off, and I relaxed about it. Now, anytime I feel disheartened about anything that I'm integrating, or learning, I remind myself that *I'm learning how to*. I don't have to know what the end goal is going to be like, or how I'll be able to do it, but rather that I'll get there by focusing on each next step I need to take.

It's also important to remember that at times it can be hard to see your progress. Real, enduring change adds up slowly over time. Observing trauma healing is about the hour hand on a clock, not the second hand. This is where keeping a journal is helpful, because it enables you to look back and see for yourself how things have changed over time.

Phases

The First Few Days

The first few days of your integration period are the most crucial. It's easy for the psyche to go right back to where it was before, pushing aside new feelings, perspectives, and insights, making them seem like a distant dream. Sometimes it can start to feel like the journey never really happened after all.

This is why it's important to plan for this and give yourself some time away from your normal life dramas, news, politics, TV, movies, and even the usual music you listen to. All of these can be triggers to pull you right back into your old, habitual states of being that close you off to the healing space you just worked so hard to open.

When I do medicine work, I always ensure that the rest of that day and the following day are set aside for solitude to allow the work I've just done to settle in. I'll go for long walks, hikes, or bike rides. I'll quietly listen to soothing instrumental music, journal, play piano, sketch, or whatever else feels good to do. I avoid having to re-engage my everyday life as long as I can to give myself time to embody the changes trying to happen.

My first guide lived an eight-hour drive from my home. I could have flown and saved myself several hours of travel time. But after trying this once, I realized that being around so many people at the airport, many of whom seemed unbelievably anxious or tense, felt awful after having been so free and open in the medicine work.

After that I learned to love the long drive home a day or two after my journey. I'd keep the music turned off and simply let my mind quietly observe whatever wanted to happen within me. Time and again I'd have feelings or memories float up, continuing the work that had started in my journey. A few times on that drive home, I had to pull over to allow big emotions to safely flow through me. Something about the quiet meditative space of a long drive, with my mind having the act of driving to focus on, was a potent experience for continuing the medicine work process.

The most important part of the first few days after medicine work is to do your best to avoid your mind settling back into the ruts of your habitual, everyday states of mind. Give yourself as much time as you possibly can to let the emotional healing that started in your session to continue to develop within you.

The First Few Weeks

The first few weeks after medicine work is when you wade back into your everyday life while staying mindful of both your habitual perspectives and defenses and the healing continuing to happen. *Here is where it can be helpful to remember that those old emotional defenses coming back aren't failures but rather are your gateways to go back in deeper again.* Resist them and they'll lock down harder. Welcome them and whatever they need to express, and you'll pass through that gateway with relative ease. This is the practice.

The Practice

Practice does not make perfect. Practice makes permanent.
Repeat the same mistakes over and over,
and you don't get any closer to Carnegie Hall.

— SARAH KAY, *No Matter the Wreckage*

It is understood that the neural connections that get used the most are the ones that the brain uses by default. The more they are used, the stronger those connections become. It takes time and effort for the changes that are happening through your medicine work to become the new default connections. Integration is a daily mindful practice that helps you stay aware of what is shifting and moving within you as well as the ways your body is perceiving and responding to your experiences.

A part of this practice is noticing when old ways of behavior, thought, and perception come into play. This isn't a time to feel defeated, become critical of yourself, or make those parts a villain. Just as in the medicine work journey, it's not about trying to get rid of one thing to replace it with something else — this is very important! The practice is to help those wounded parts to heal so they function naturally and authentically instead of from a place of perceived threat and vulnerability. It's about simply doing your best to permit the expression of whatever needs to release emotional energy without letting it take over perception and thus thoughts, feelings, and behaviors.

Clearly, there are times you probably don't want to give something trying to bubble up full external expression: at work, on a subway, or when out to dinner with friends. Just as in the medicine work session itself, the key is coming back to your breath, slowing things down and allowing the feeling to exist. The key is to let it radiate that emotional energy within the infinite space within you, like a distant star radiating heat out into the universe, mindfully holding this aspect of you with compassion just as you would a hurting child.

Then, when you are at a place and time where it is safe to do so, you can express it more fully. It's the same process of finding and passing through each next gateway. Practicing a body-centered therapy, allowing yourself to cry, screaming into a pillow, or vigorously exercising are all good ways to get the emotions flowing. As are journaling, sketching, or talking with your support person.

I've found that integrating the new ways of functioning and perceiving that emerged from psychedelic experiences is in many ways similar to learning to play the piano. Each time I step up to something new and more challenging, I can feel overwhelmed and defeated if I try to take it all in at once. How can I possibly play something like this? It seems impossible!

It is when I slow everything way down, break it into smaller, more manageable pieces, and practice slowly and mindfully that it eventually comes together. Instead of focusing on the end goal and being overwhelmed by all the stuff that I don't know how to do to get there, I keep that intention in mind while only focusing on the next step that I need to take, and then the one after that, and the one after that.

The process of healing will find its own way, just as water finds its way downhill, when you bring mindful practice to your integration efforts. It's all about continuing to let the emotional energy move and express and not be stifled by habitual defense mechanisms. The more you can create space for both your old defensive habits and the healing process trying to happen to exist and express, the greater the benefits you'll see accumulate in your life.

Sleep on It

If mindfully allowing yourself to continue to express and heal is the yin of integration, the yang is good, deep sleep. It's been understood for some time that it is during sleep that the brain integrates what has been learned from your recent experiences. Sleep is a powerful force multiplier in true healing and growth.

Even with piano practice, getting good sleep enables my brain to integrate the new skills, understandings, and nuance of control that I'm learning through careful, mindful practice each day. If I were to keep practicing mistakes over and over again, that's what I'd be integrating. By mindfully playing small pieces at a time slowly, my body learns how to make the music, and this is integrated as I sleep. It never fails that as the days and weeks go by, the music that once seemed impossibly complex starts to become natural for me to be able to play.

Integration Help

The integration process can be challenging, but I've found that there are really effective ways you can help the process along and take off the rough edges.

Self-Care

Show compassion for yourself, especially the aspects of you trying to heal. Be gentle and understanding if your emotions get away from you. Take good care of yourself as you would a valued friend, family member, or a hurting child. Eating good, healthy food and engaging in fun, enjoyable activities can promote a calm and centered mind and body. This is the time to celebrate the authentic, healthy you that is working to emerge.

Support

Engage with your support resources as often as you can. Working through challenges with a trusted therapist and talking things out with someone close to you can make the difference between staying in the process of the healing work and closing expressing emotions off out of habit, discomfort, or fear.

Getting Centered

I recommend setting up a meditation or other mindful practice routine to do daily, or even multiple times per day. It's an important aspect of emotional and psychological hygiene. Anxiety, stress, doubt, and old habits can start creeping in slowly and take over before you even realize it's happened. By taking some time to get centered on your breath and surrender into the moment, you'll be bringing yourself back to your healing baseline. Getting re-centered in this way regularly is an important part of the practice of integration and an easy way to stay ahead of the buildup of the fear that empowers defense mechanisms.

Exercise

In the first several weeks after a journey, exercise can be really helpful. Even though in the moment this can often feel like the last thing that you want to do, getting your heart rate up, at least a little, for twenty minutes or more a day can play a big role in deepening the integration process. It can help you to unclench, step back, and observe as you anchor in your body on each breath in and out. Just like mindfulness exercises or meditation, exercise can be a potent way to release anxiety-born tensions.

I've had many experiences of just wanting to be as still as is possible, as if I was going to miss something important if I was moving around. But on my guide's insistence, I would go for a walk or a low-impact workout and found that the energy that had begun to be released in my journey was still trying to move. Anything that got my heart rate up a bit seemed to help the energy to move and my emotions to be freed up. I would feel better, not because I was avoiding whatever was trying to process in my body, but because I was giving it room to flow naturally.

Bodywork

Good, deep massage can be unbelievably helpful in your healing process because the emotional energy trapped in the body is often held in by tension in the muscles and fascia. This could be from a professional massage therapist or from someone close to you. You can also do really good work on yourself.

There is a lot of information available about self-massage, as well as many tools to help facilitate it, such as foam rollers, trigger-point canes, massage balls, and a variety of other options.

Get in the Flow

Being in a flow state is when you are completely focused on whatever task you are doing. It's being "in the zone," which gets you out of your head and away from fears, concerns, or frustrations around integration. Flow state activities are great ways to release the tiller on your healing process and permit it to continue along its natural course.

My favorite flow state activities are riding motorcycles, usually quite fast, practicing music, and exercising. In each of these, I end up disappearing, and there is only the activity being performed. Afterwards I feel renewed, centered and calm.

Creative Expression

Creative expression is a truly potent tool to utilize during integration. It doesn't have to be professional art, it's not for anyone else but you. It's perfect so long as it comes from the parts of you in the process of healing. Sing songs or sound tones that move that part of you, experiment to see what works. Try sketching, painting, writing, or whatever art inspires you. Just let out whatever is trying to move through you with your artistic expression.

Keeping Your Gains

Regressing to habitual states of feeling and being can creep in subtly over time, making it hard to notice. Having a way to detect these changes early on can empower you to take action and correct your course. I think of these early-warning strategies as canaries in the coal mine, a set of easily identifiable markers that let me know if I'm beginning to slide backwards. This is how the healing process continues well beyond the first month after having done medicine work.

You've probably heard the stories of miners in the time before electronic sensors, who used to take caged canaries down into the mines with them. Being much more sensitive to poor air quality than humans, if any dangerous changes in air quality began to happen, like carbon monoxide building up in the mine, the canaries would die. And the miners, seeing the warning, could move themselves back to safe ground before they, too, succumbed.

Luckily for you, and canaries in general, you don't have to sacrifice animals in this endeavor. These are metaphorical birds that you set up to help you detect when old patterns of thinking, feeling, or behaving are trying to reestablish themselves. (And I prefer to think that I revive my canaries should I see them passed out in their cages!)

My first-ever "canary" was simply not making my bed. I'd never been one to make my bed each morning. But as my overall mental and emotional wellness improved, I found myself surprisingly wanting my bedroom (and the rest of my home) to be neater and more organized. After waking up in the morning, I couldn't walk away from my bed without first making it. When that desire dropped away, it was a signal that something was not quite right. And because my old depressive states would historically sneak up slowly, and I wouldn't realize that I was in one until it had its hooks in me really deeply, this early warning system became integral to not sliding backwards into depression. It has worked beautifully.

In the last several years it's only happened a couple of times: I'd pause before starting to make my bed, thinking that I should just leave it. Each time, I took a deep breath and renewed my commitment to keeping myself moving in a positive direction. I'd make the bed for sure. Then I'd get some exercise, go out in nature, or do whatever else I needed to do to recharge and bring my mood up to where I function the best.

Since then, I've enlisted several additional canaries around how I eat, exercise, practice music, etc. Anytime a positive change naturally happens through the medicine work, I'll let it get established, and if it feels like a good marker for how I'm functioning now, that will become one of my canaries too.

Canaries can vary in sensitivity, so you are able to see some being affected sooner than others, which gives you a sense of scale or depth of any distress. If you see multiple metaphorical birds lying feet-up in their cages, it should be a big red flag that something within you needs compassion and care right now! And it's an indicator of the gateway that you can use to go inwards to help whatever is trying to express itself to heal.

Part Three

*Our wounds are often the openings
into the best and most beautiful part of us.*

— DAVID RICHO, *The Power of Coincidence:
How Life Shows Us What We Need to Know*

CHAPTER 17

COMING FULL CIRCLE

After that first group experience on 5-MeO-DMT, I was drawn towards using psychedelics to heal with a powerful drive and sense of urgency to keep pressing forward and not allow this door that had been opened for me to close again. I'd had a direct experience of using psychedelics in a new way that could actually contact the deep emotional wounding that had remained out of reach for my entire life. This gave me something beyond mere hope that I could heal. I could feel it with certainty. I signed up for a one-on-one session with this guide.

My first one-on-one session again used 5-MeO-DMT in the form of vaporized toad venom. This time we did three rounds of it. The first was pretty light, the second a solid moderate dose, and the third a full breakthrough dose. It was another incredible day of cathartic release, reaching into areas that had always been defended and inaccessible before.

My second one-on-one guided session was just over a month later. Here we worked with MDMA, 175 milligrams to start, with a 50 milligram booster later. This is when my guide used tuning forks to help open up the energetic flow of sensation throughout my whole body. It was the first time in memory that I had permitted myself to genuinely be seen and heard by another person, to be truly vulnerable. And it was the first time that I directly encountered and saw clearly the shame that exerted so much control over my life.

After this incredible session I felt that huge progress had been made. But I also felt much like someone who'd been dying of thirst that had been given only a small sip of water. The physical imperative to drink more was all-consuming. I needed to keep the momentum of the medicine work going. I began to do solo journeys with 5-MeO-DMT, MDMA and mushrooms. I wouldn't do these too often, but the massive energies trying to move within me sometimes couldn't wait for my next guided psychedelic sessions either.

Clearly this wasn't without risks, and I had to proceed carefully. But the agony that I'd always kept buried deep inside had been shown a path towards relief, towards healing, and that became the most important thing I could do with my life. Throughout the entirety of the intensive phase of my healing process, I worked with psychedelic medicines around once a month, either with my guide or by myself, setting aside an entire day for it. Occasionally my solo work would be more frequent, but I was always cautious and aware of it possibly interfering with the integration of the previous work.

I wasn't pulled towards the psychedelic experiences themselves. Most days I felt I'd be happy if I never took another psychedelic ever again in my life. Any recreational or expansive pleasure in their use had faded away and would not return for quite a while. Psychedelics had instead become tools helping me to do important, lifesaving work.

These early psychedelic healing sessions were focused on the emotional isolation that defined my life. I would feel into the loneliness and despair to set my compass, my intentions, that would guide the work ahead. Each of these journeys was defined by the massive energetic releases and deep outpourings of sadness, frustration, confusion, and conflicting thoughts and emotions.

Each session provided an unburdening of things previously held deep inside. My guide was a compassionate and empathetic witness to whatever needed to be expressed. It wasn't ever about dwelling in old miseries and stories; they were instead expressed and released to the degree that they could be. Some would release right then and there, never needing to be revisited again. With others, my mind would begin relaxing around them so they could eventually be released in future work.

Going Deeper …

Throughout my adult life, I often wondered why my particular upbringing had caused the intensity of dysfunction for me that it had. I felt that others had gone through more horrific experiences and had come through still able to have hope and to find connection, friendship, and love. I didn't understand why my experience of life was so devastatingly diminished and why isolation, fear, hopelessness, and despair were the foundation that everything else was built upon. To me, the intensity of the effect always seemed to be out of proportion to the cause.

Session after session, layer after layer, I worked my way ever deeper inwards. Soon the call from within was no longer about loneliness and isolation but rather was simply a call for help. Over and over again in guided and solo sessions, the words *help me* would issue from my lips, yet I had no real understanding of who within me was asking for help or what specific help was needed.

Eventually, during an integration support session, I spontaneously said, *I think that my grandfather molested me when I was quite young.* I had no emotional attachment to it, nor any memory of it; the words just came out like that. Deep inside I could feel the truth of it, but at the level of my everyday mind, I couldn't accept that it could be true. I had loved my grandpa, and he was known as a gentleman farmer and a trustworthy businessman, a man of principle. It just couldn't be true. My guide would frequently remind me to hold it all lightly, neither accepting it as true or false but only as a possibility, so I wouldn't force a belief or impede further truth from emerging. *Something* had happened to me for sure — of that there was no doubt at all. I needed more time and exploration to get to the truth of it.

In subsequent psychedelic healing sessions, I would always come to a place of absolute certainty, feeling the truth of it in my body, in my very cells. Fragments of memories began to float to the surface, and intense moments of emotional expression would burst out. I had many experiences of crying with overwhelming fear, rage, and shame. And I had paradoxical experiences of deep, intense guilt about what had happened.

As sessions went by, memories would come to the surface where my grandpa's own guilt and shame led him to angrily lash out at me and say hateful things. Seeing the rage, pain, and shame on his face, much as with the anger that was frequently expressed towards me in my everyday life, I accepted responsibility for this having happened because of something about me.

I accepted as truth that my grandfather had loved me and that he'd only done what he had because something about me made him do it, that it was my fault. I'd find myself in these psychedelic sessions sobbing uncontrollably, truly expressing a broken heart and begging him to forgive me for causing this to happen and hurting him so. This is how it works with children. They are developmentally wired to be egocentric, so everything that happens in their lives is about them and because of them. It's one of the more insidious legacies of sexual, physical, and emotional abuse.

… and Deeper

For months I struggled on a seesaw of moments of deep clarity where I could feel the truth of what my grandfather had done in one moment, and then at other times, I would be up in my head about it, suffering deep doubt and going through endless rationalizations of how it couldn't be true.

I eventually brought this up with my mother and she responded, *Oh my god, your uncle told me years ago that the same thing had happened to him, and I didn't want to believe him. I thought that he was just trying to cause trouble in the family.* She said that he had given many details, even remembering smells that still haunted him decades later.

It was then that I knew everything that had come up in my sessions around this was absolutely true and that there was no need to doubt myself any longer. Releasing the conflict allowed the unwinding of a deep tension in me. A major missing puzzle piece had finally found its place, and so much that I'd struggled with in my life finally began making sense. The deep sense of relief I felt from my core was profound and life changing.

This was a pivotal point in my life that took an unimaginable amount of effort, tears, courage, and amazingly talented support to get to. I'd have plenty more work to come, to find a place of acceptance, and ultimately peace, around it. Eventually I would face the conflict between still feeling and having felt love for my grandfather, and the rage, humiliation, and shame around what he'd done to me.

In a much later session, I voiced this conflict to my medicine guide, and what she told me alleviated the incongruity that was holding up my healing process. She said, *It's not uncommon to love people who have hurt us. The two things are separate and both valid.* When I stopped putting energy into the idea of a conflict that had to be reconciled, I was able to come to the point of acceptance. This is where the true healing became possible. As my internal "no" and refusal to accept the reality of the abuse diminished, it steadily became something that had happened to me and stopped being something still alive in me now. I stopped wishing that it could have been different and then let it move from the present to the past.

… and Deeper Still

Both my guide and I thought that we'd reached the core of things, that the worst was behind me, and that from that point on, it would all be just cleanup work. This felt absolutely real to me, and oh boy, were we wrong! This is why it's so important for a guide to never interpret or make assumptions about their client's process.

During this time my guide had been going through some intense personal issues and was planning to travel for several months to clear his head and get centered in his life and work once more. I asked if we could do a first-ever double session before he left. The plan was to do 3-MMC, ketamine and some 5-MeO-DMT the first day. Take a day to recover, go for a hike and have time to myself. Then, do a second day on ketamine and a lighter dose of mushrooms. The intent was that this would help open me deeply and give me plenty to work on in my extended integration period for the few months until his return.

The first day was spectacular, with many feelings around the trauma and abuse with my grandfather being expressed. At the start I had on an eye mask and a weighted blanket, which were comforting and grounding. This helped me to drop deeply into the work and helped me to stay focused inward.

The second day of healing work, however, was a nightmare. I used the same eye mask and weighted blanket, but instead of providing comfort, they sparked an overwhelming sense of claustrophobia, of being trapped. I took them both off, but it was too late. Less than an hour into the session, I was thrust into a level of terror that I couldn't remember coming anywhere close to ever before.

I'd experienced plenty of moments of intense fear in psychedelic healing work and had learned to navigate it really well, especially with the help of my guide. But what was being felt this day was radically more intense. Even describing the difference in this way doesn't feel like it's close to the reality of it. It was the difference between the feelings of fear while waiting to skydive for the first time and the pure terror someone must feel when they realize that they forgot to put on their parachute just after having jumped out of the plane. *It was the terror of imminent death from the perspective of a child experiencing it.*

This went on for hours, coming in big waves, and nothing my guide did helped at all. I spent most of this time curled in a fetal position, gasping for breath, and just trying to hold on. This was made worse by the fact that, for the first time ever in our work together, my guide felt truly out of touch with my experience. Distracted by his own personal issues and emotionally already having one foot out the door for the tropical paradise he was leaving for in a couple of days, he had no clue about the intensity of what I was experiencing.

Throughout the day the terror would come in waves. In my mind I could see someone as a shadow in a white haze, like looking through a frosted glass door. When their identity would start to bubble up, the intensity of the terror would amplify, and I'd find myself crying, *I don't want to know!* over and over again as my mind worked desperately to shove the information back down again. I had no conscious awareness of what it was that I didn't want to know, let alone who did it.

Several times I unthinkingly reached up with both hands and started choking myself with considerable force. I did it to the point that I'd start gasping and fighting for breath, as if I had no control over what was happening. My guide did his best, with the limited internal resources he had that day, to help. Because he was so out of tune with me and what I was going through, I was alone to suffer in what I was experiencing. I was desperately in over my head and, just as it had been when this abuse originally occurred, I was without anyone to understand or know to help.

At one point I begged for a Xanax to help this all to settle down, so I could perhaps find a place from where more work was possible. I had never previously asked for anything to help control or tone down a session before, and he had no idea just how much trouble I was in. He refused because we hadn't come to an agreement about possibly using Xanax when I was sober. But I have always believed if this had happened at a time when he was empathetically engaged with me, as I had always felt was the case in all of our other sessions, he likely would have gotten me one, or five, without question.

I never did let the identity of this abuser surface that day. What did come through clearly was that I'd been sexually abused by someone else, besides my grandfather, and that at some point, things had turned violent. This instilled such terror, and the perception that death was imminent, that it caused a fracture in my psyche and the memory of it was locked away deep, deep inside.

This was my first and, so far, only experience of mishandled psychedelic healing work causing further trauma. It created a significant fear of working with mushrooms at all, which took a long time to overcome. It planted a new, underlying concern that a guide might not always have my back if things got really difficult. It was the first time I didn't have absolute trust in my safety and care during a guided journey, and that left its own wounds.

A Full-Time Job

I met with my guide the next day, before he left on his trip. We took a walk along the ocean and discussed my concerns about how out of sync I had felt that we'd been, and I made clear how overwhelmed and out of my depth I'd been in the session. He acknowledged that he didn't read the signs well and recommended I make investigating what had been revealed in the session my full-time job for the next several months while he was gone. I took this to heart and did just that.

First, I shifted the bulk of the responsibilities for my business over to my office manager. For a couple of years, I barely set foot in my office and only worked remotely from home, and only then when it was absolutely necessary.

Next, I sought out the kinds of support I felt would enable me to gently and safely approach this delicate, heavily defended and easily triggered wounded place within me. I started working weekly with a Somatic Experiencing trauma therapist, an EMDR (eye movement desensitization and reprocessing) therapist, a good deep-tissue body worker and a breathwork facilitator. Over time, these all helped to soften the defenses and played a big role in allowing the medicine work to help me to heal.

I also made significant lifestyle changes, most geared towards helping me to get better and more rejuvenating sleep to enhance my integration process. I stopped drinking alcohol and cut way back on my caffeine consumption (stopping at 11:00 a.m. each day where previously my cut-off time was 4:00 p.m.). I began exercising daily, improved my diet, and started intermittent fasting, usually having my meals between 2:00 p.m. and 7:00 p.m. These changes made a significant difference in the quality of my sleep and in the energy and clarity I felt during the day.

Onwards and Inwards

Neither my guide nor I had any idea of the Pandora's box of complex layers of intense trauma-based fear and emotion that we were opening when we started working together. Nor were we prepared for the depth and intensity of the trauma energy that was unwinding in me and that kept increasing with each session. My guide was either unable or unwilling to refer me out to a trauma-focused medicine guide when I asked about it. So, it was up to me to find the support I needed.

It was heartbreaking for me to make the choice to leave him, someone that I truly love and admire. I have nothing but the deepest gratitude for him and all of the healing and growth he had helped me to achieve. In two years of working together, we did nineteen incredibly intimate and powerfully healing one-on-one sessions. I did an additional eight solo sessions during that time. The psychedelic healing work done in this period not only radically and irrevocably improved my experience of life, it saved my life.

I set a clear intention within myself to find someone with the rare and specific skill set that I needed. I also intended to find someone who was both much closer to where I lived and hopefully willing to work with me to do medicine work sessions at my home. I wanted to be able to seamlessly move between the work, integration, and the rest of my life without affecting the momentum of it all.

To prepare for this intensive work, I converted some large storage rooms off my garage into my personal development space. They were already plumbed for a toilet, shower, and sink, so I had the space made over with one room as a bathroom that would also hold a sensory deprivation floatation tank for deeply focused meditation. The other larger room was double-walled and insulated for both extreme privacy and quiet. I painted the rooms a calming, soothing color and added a surround sound system with the speakers all built into the walls and ceiling. Last came natural wood flooring, a comfy sofa, a ceiling fan, and a mini-split air conditioning and heating system. Once I added a queen-sized supportive and comfortable mat on the floor, I felt the space was complete. A friend dubbed it my "launchpad."

As the rooms were being built, I started networking to find a medicine guide, asking people I trusted if they knew of anyone. Around a month later, I was introduced to a fantastically qualified, experienced and trained medicine guide who had done a great deal of her own deep work as well.

She agreed to work with me at my home in my launchpad, and on our first guided session, I could clearly tell that we were going to be able to make amazing headway with the trauma that I was needing to work my way into in order to heal. There was a noticeable difference between the masculine and feminine energy in the sessions. Not one better than another, just a different quality to it. But it was in the space she held for the intense trauma energy that needed to move and express in me that the real differences and possibilities began to show.

Because she'd done work within herself that was as deep and deeper than where I myself was trying to go, the permission in the space for those deep places in me to open was radically different than it had been before. I wasn't aware of this limitation when working with my former guide, and to be fair, he had held a deep space for me up until we had started hitting the trauma from sexual abuse.

With the opportunity to compare the two experiences, I could recognize the unspoken, subliminal limits that had kept me from feeling safe going deeper in my previous work. He simply hadn't gone this deep in himself yet, even though he'd done journeys with massive doses of medicines, so he couldn't hold a safe space for me to go there too. And, he wasn't trained or experienced in specifically working with trauma. If I had stopped doing psychedelic healing work after him, I never would have known that so much more healing was possible.

This is the difference between what a qualified psychedelic guide and a true medicine guide can offer. And, this is why I have been so thorough in describing the differences between those who are qualified to be guides of any kind, and those who are not. Had I been working with one of the many radically unqualified self-proclaimed "guides" when I started out, the unconscious limitations they would have unknowingly imposed on the work would have kept me from ever even attempting to approach the deep, unhealed traumas I held. I would have missed out on the chance to heal and have an amazingly improved experience of life, and I'm not certain that I would even still be alive today. My heart's desire in writing all of this is to help prevent that from happening to others.

During this new phase of my healing and growth, I also engaged with a number of other guides, following my instincts for the experiences I needed. I did quite a few solo sessions, as well as working in some co-journeys with people when I felt we could hold a beneficial space for each other. My primary medicine guide was always kept in the loop with what I was doing and how the work was going, so we were always on the same page in our work together. It was with her that I made the vast majority of the progress I describe next.

The Black Hole

Working my way into this recently discovered and heavily defended trauma wound was the greatest challenge by far of anything that had come up in any of the medicine work I'd done to date. Dissociation was my primary defense, and it exerted an unbelievable amount of control over me. When the medicines opened access past that dissociation for even the briefest of moments, that overwhelming terror would come rushing out to push me back into "safe" waters once more.

It was obvious that something significant was there because of the incredibly powerful coping mechanisms and defenses around it, but I couldn't see or feel anything actually in it. It was much like scientists trying to identify a black hole deep in outer space. They can only tell that it's there by observing what is orbiting around it, with no information coming directly from the thing itself.

Another metaphor that serves is that of a science fiction force field or energy shield. Anytime I attempted to directly approach this wound, my mind would bounce off of it and be redirected instantly into other thoughts. Or, I would just zone out. Both in medicine work and in the body-centered therapies that I was doing at the time, I'd only become aware of having been redirected in this way after the fact, often when it was pointed out to me by whomever I was working with. At times, I would be mid-sentence and just start talking about something else entirely.

Over time I became better able to see it happening for myself, both when doing healing work and in everyday life. Eventually in medicine work, I was able to slow it down (or speed up my observation of it) to actually witness the psychological function as it was occurring. It was fascinating to observe these processes as they happened, step by step.

What became evident was that the direct approach wasn't going to work and that I'd have to learn how to advance carefully, never looking directly at it. I'd have to invite whoever or whatever was inside to come out, to be healed, without any attempt to actually see, know or understand anything about him until he said it was okay.

It was a complex and incredibly delicate process, moving one tiny, careful step at a time, with each advance releasing massive energy. For over a year, I was doing guided medicine work at least monthly, with frequent solo medicine work as well anytime I felt like there was more that was ready to move. My weekly deep-tissue body work, regular exercise regimen, improved sleep, and body-centered therapy sessions helped to make this frequency of incredibly intensive medicine work even possible.

Intensive Focus

It took months of focused, deep work to start making any real progress into this heavily defended space. Though during that time, a lot of potent healing was still happening, with these issues being resolved in order to enable me to have access to that deeper, heavily defended area.

I had found acceptance around what my grandfather had done to me, no longer resisting the truth of it. I came to a place of honest forgiveness, understanding that his compulsions had come from his own deep wounding from what certainly must have happened to him as well, when he was young. This wasn't something that I thought my way through, it wasn't a lofty concept based on any belief of what I was supposed to do to be a compassionate person, and it wasn't a bypass. This forgiveness came on the heels of the acceptance, from deep within, emanating from that now-healing part of me that his behaviors had wounded.

I had also found forgiveness for myself, for things I had done that I had been carrying a sense of guilt and shame about, sometimes for decades. I saw so clearly how I had been dragging them around with me like a boat anchor, hanging on to them as a form of punishment. This was when I began seeing myself as a fallible human being in a world full of fellow fallible humans and cut myself a lot more slack.

I had also made real progress in forgiving my mother, who had made attempts at apologizing for some of her behaviors over the years. It took a long time to not just see, but truly feel, her as a deeply wounded human being who was at times rageful and violent out of her own pain and overwhelm, as opposed to someone who'd been vicious, hurtful, and hateful because of something about me that had made her feel that way. I'd had an intellectual understanding of this for a long time. But feeling the truth of it was something different entirely, and that came from the healing and accepting process.

I have made big strides forward in forgiving others, releasing resentment and anger over having felt wronged or slighted by them in the past. When my anger had been largely hidden as a shadow, it would come out passive-aggressively towards these people as hurtful humor, biting observations, and criticism. That behavior was an unconscious effort to move them from having the power to hurt me, to being perceived as beneath me and thus safe. I was unconsciously trying to beat them down emotionally, so they'd never want to be hurtful towards me again. As that shadow continued to come out of the darkness and integrate into the whole of me, the compulsion to vent passive-aggressively like this all but disappeared.

Just like any other human being, I can still be triggered into unhelpful behaviors if I'm put into an overwhelming enough situation. But the nature of my defense mechanisms has changed profoundly. Being triggered is much less likely to happen, and if it does, I would see it right away and do my heartfelt best to apologize, learn from it, and make amends. It's all significant progress considering where I came from, and this is a realistic view of what this kind of healing really looks like.

Revelations

Across several medicine work sessions, I'd begun permitting the terror to slowly titrate into my conscious awareness, keeping the flow of its release at a manageable rate, so I could stay present and not trigger those defenses to dissociate me from it. This was always made possible both by my clear intention to hold a safe, gentle space for that fear, and by my medicine guide being right there, usually before I even knew that I needed her, to help me relax, breathe, and surrender.

I began making my way through the layers into the heart of this emotional wound. *No, no, no, it can't be true!* began coming out over and over again. I'd clench up, resisting the truth from coming to the surface as it so clearly needed to do. Each time, as the resistance relaxed and released, it evolved into another loop of *NO!* being said over and over again. Not a "no" to what happened, but an emphatic refusal to accept the truth, whatever that was. Then as that released, it turned into *No, I don't want it!* which I said repeatedly as I was writhing on the floor trying to escape the discomfort of the confines of my own skin.

Repeating statements like this many times was common in my deep work. These were the words that resonated with the emotions being expressed. Trying to put any different words to it, or in any way trying to figure out what the words actually meant, would have broken my connection to the truth being expressed from my body. I had to go for the ride, allowing each layer to fully express itself however it needed to, so the next deeper layer could be approached.

Finally, I came to rage. I could feel it wanting to be expressed, and I could feel my body wanting desperately to keep it from coming out. I knew instinctively that I'd have to get moving, or it would close off. So, I grabbed the yellow plastic Wiffle bat that I kept at the foot of the mat I was on. I quickly looked at my medicine guide, so we both knew that I was in control and that she was safe. And then I proceeded to beat the hell out of a pillow.

You goddamn fucking bitch, how could you do that to me!?!? over and over turned into *You used me like a thing*, and as the rage, shame, and humiliation started to subside, it evolved into *Oh my god, this really happened to me.* The feeling of disbelief and agony was profound as I found myself saying, *She stole my whole life from me and never cared at all.*

And then the truth was out. A woman in my family, someone who was trusted to care for me, had molested me many times over the years. What was truly terrifying was how it all happened. It was like a switch would go off and "she" would go away. The lights were on, but nobody was home. She would hold me down and use me in whatever way suited her. I was nothing more than a thing to be used, and the fear, humiliation, and shame were things that she seemed to feed on. Afterwards the switch would flip back and she would carry on like nothing at all had happened, which left me feeling deeply confused, despairing, and alone to suffer in what had happened.

At one point I cried and struggled, which I believed caused her to momentarily be aware of what she was doing, to have to *feel* about what she was doing, which triggered something deep and dark in her. Her face a cold, calculating mask, she gripped my throat with both hands and squeezed. With all of the compassion in her eyes of a snake preparing to eat a mouse, she strangled me as a determination was being made if I was going to be a problem or not, if I should be ended or not.

My life, my *self*, had no value whatsoever; I would have to stop triggering her or I would die. Even a young mind has an animal's instinct of death, and I was directly experiencing it with an existential terror. This, I believe, is when my mind fully adapted to dissociate, and I learned to "die" to be safe. I had to go limp and expressionless, as if dead inside, for her to stop. In many earlier medicine work sessions, I'd expressed that I believed that I was supposed to be dead, that I wasn't supposed to be here in this life, that I didn't belong here. And now it all resolved into a terrifyingly clear picture.

In future medicine work sessions as I revisited this, going ever deeper, I began to recognize how I had learned to never acknowledge what happened in any way, not even within myself. I could never look sad or bothered in the slightest; this part of me had to be "dead" to survive.

This is where that seemingly dead, mummified child within me came from, that I'd first unearthed in Taffy's office all those years ago. I had learned very early, and then had it reinforced through repeated experiences, that I had to be dead, or someone would find me and want to use me. I had to be dead or she might kill me for real. What had been buried alive, frozen in time in a state of pure terror of being seen to be alive, was the part of me capable of unguarded connection and love, the part capable of feeling safe to feel and express joy or enjoyment. It was the part capable of being openly vulnerable with someone else. It was the part that makes being alive worthwhile.

Anytime this part of me would try to emerge, an overwhelming feeling of shame would close him off again. This was the shame he felt while being abused, turned into a defense mechanism to protect him from being seen and thus drawing more abuse to himself. It was an unfathomable well of claustrophobic shame that kept him pushed to the bottom, out of sight and safe from groping hands. It was this sense of shame for just being alive that had so completely infected every aspect of my experience of life. It shaped and colored how I felt about absolutely everything, distorting everything into a potential and likely threat.

It took a lot of work and many more guided and solo sessions, but we finally broke through. The life energy that is that vital piece of my humanity came bursting out, just as it had in Taffy's office all those years ago. I felt like a sun had ignited at the core of me and was radiating so powerfully that I might burst apart and return to the source of *all that is*. And in the core of that wound, after waiting so long for anyone to care enough to help him, to save him, was a perfect, beautiful little boy with a heart as big as the universe itself, as deserving of love and connection as anyone who'd ever lived or ever would. And my medicine guide and I were both there to welcome him back to life.

CHAPTER 18

COMING FULL CIRCLE BACK TO YOU

I didn't know, I couldn't know, when I started all of this, where it would eventually lead. It was a long, painful, and challenging path that eventually brought me full circle back to myself, back to my heart. It has been the single most challenging and rewarding endeavor of my entire life.

I continue to do guided medicine work, but not with the same monomaniacal intensity as before. For a long time, I felt like a trauma clown car, never believing how much more could possibly still keep emerging. Incredibly, there was more to this story that was eventually revealed, but I finally made it to the core of my wounding and started working my way back out again. Certainly, there was more healing to do; there still is. But now my focus is on both healing and actually living my life, for which I feel a crushing gratitude.

I love spending time with my own family, engaging with dear friends, learning and playing music, expressing myself creatively, playing with my dogs, and riding motorcycles. I'm even starting to open to the idea of finding my soulmate. I am nurtured by learning and creative expression and am looking forward to sharing more, to being of service more, as I move into a future that I'm genuinely excited about and curious to greet.

Yes, it took me a long time to work my way through to the core of my suffering. This was in part owing to the early life circumstances when the initial traumas occurred. It was also in part due to the unimaginable intensity of the terror and humiliation that had at times been inflicted upon me. This caused a need for defenses that could match that intensity to protect me from it, which, layer by layer, had to be carefully navigated through. And, it was in part because I was unaware for several months that I needed a more qualified guide, one capable of holding space for the trauma I was trying to process.

Others have healed their traumas in medicine work and come to satisfactory resolutions in a much shorter period of time and with far fewer sessions being required. Everyone's individual process will be entirely unique to them.

So, let's bring this all back to *you*. From the bottom of my heart, I wish for anyone who is suffering from the devastating effects of trauma and deep emotional wounding to feel the kind of healing and the life-changing benefits that I have, and more. But coming to that healing with psychedelics is not going to be the right approach for everyone. Or, it might not be the right approach for someone right now, but could be once they have done the necessary work of building a good foundation of self-awareness, understanding, and tolerance for their own emotional states. You can find the right path for you, if it is your honest intention to do so.

Psychedelics may not be the instant miracle cure that they are so often touted to be. But I sincerely believe that, when properly used and supported, they can indeed help miracles happen for those who are willing and ready.

If, upon doing your due diligence, you come to the determination that this is the right approach to healing for you, then know that you go with my whole heart supporting you. In the darkest, most challenging times, know that I've been through them, too, and now feel only gratitude for those experiences, as I believe you will too. With all my heart, I hope that what I've shared of myself here is of profound service to you in your own quest to heal.

CHAPTER 42

Surrender and allow.

Out beyond ideas of wrongdoing and rightdoing,
there is a field. I'll meet you there.
When the soul lies down in that grass,
the world is too full to talk about.
Ideas, language, even the phrase "each other"
doesn't make any sense.
The breeze at dawn has secrets to tell you.
Don't go back to sleep.
You must ask for what you really want.
Don't go back to sleep.
People are going back and forth across the doorsill
where the two worlds touch.
The door is round and open.
Don't go back to sleep.

— RUMI

Author Shannon Duncan
in his "launchpad"

About the Author

Shannon Duncan is an entrepreneur and the author of the landmark book *Present Moment Awareness*. In his newest book, *Coming Full Circle*, Duncan shares what he learned during his own intensive, multiyear process of healing trauma with the help of psychedelics. An advocate for those seeking to heal from trauma, he sincerely hopes that sharing what he learned through his experiences will be of service to those who are in need.

Shannon lives in California and enjoys spending time with his family, engaging with friends, learning and playing music, expressing himself artistically, cooking, playing with his dogs, and riding fast motorcycles.

www.shannonduncan.com

Acknowledgments

There are many people whom I'd like to thank for their help both in my growth process and in the development of this book.

First, I want to express my gratitude to Taffy Clarke Pelton for reviewing this work and helping me to stay accurate and to not speak as an expert where clearly I am not. Your support over the years has meant the world to me.

To my Medicine Guide, whom I'll call "Katie" because she asked me not to call her Shirley. Surely you must know my heart, my authentic self, so well by now that you know how much your help has meant to me. You stand among the few, with Taffy, who actually give what so many only promise: true help to actually heal and have a vastly improved experience of life. I am so grateful to have you in my life, my friend.

To my first guide, thank you for opening the door and showing me how real, deep healing is possible. You saved my life and I'll never forget that.

I'd also like to thank the following people for their support:

My dear friends Leanne, Rod, and Charlie for all the amazing feedback and insight on what I've written. It really helped to make this book the best that it could be.

Nancy Marriott: In the early stages of the book-writing process I hired Nancy as a writing coach. She helped me to see that I really can be a writer! http://nancymarriott.com

Cherie Kephart: An exceptional developmental editor. She truly helped bring cohesiveness and clarity to the book. https://cheriekephart.com

Isabella Furth, Ph.D: A copyeditor who did a fantastic, meticulous job helping me clean up the manuscript and bring it to completion. http://bluefisheditorial.com

Asa Wild: Created the final interior layout. http://www.asawild.org

David Reuther: My singing coach. Thank you for being so cool and helping me to find my voice! https://davidreuthervocals.com

Credits

Page 94: Connie Zweig excerpt from *Meeting the Shadow: The Hidden Power of the Dark Side of Human Nature,* edited by Connie Zweig and Jeremiah Abrams, copyright © 1991 by Connie Zweig and Jeremiah Abrams. Used by permission of Tarcher, an imprint of Penguin Publishing Group, a division of Penguin Random House LLC. All rights reserved.

Page 105: Stephen Cope excerpts from *The Great Work of Your Life: A Guide for the Journey to Your True Calling* by Stephen Cope, copyright © 2012 by Stephen Cope. Used by permission of Bantam Books, an imprint of Random House, a division of Penguin Random House LLC. All rights reserved.

Page 194: Sarah Kay poem "Postcards" from the anthology *No Matter the Wreckage* by Sarah Kay, copyright © 2017, page 76. Reprinted by arrangement with Write Bloody Publishing, www.writebloody.com

Page 201: David Richo excerpt from *The Power of Coincidence: How Life Shows Us What We Need to Know* by David Richo, copyright © 1998, 2007 by David Richo. Reprinted by arrangement with The Permissions Company, LLC on behalf of Shambhala Publications Inc., Boulder, Colorado, shambhala.com

Page 227: The Rumi quote is from a translation by Coleman Barks.

The thoughts from Maslow and Jung are commonly used paraphrasings of quotes often attributed to them.

The FocusTool

APPLE APP STORE   GOOGLE PLAY STORE

SCAN THE QR CODE TO DOWNLOAD THE "FOCUS TOOL" APP

The Focus Tool™ was originally a device I created that readers could purchase to support the exercises in the book *Present Moment Awareness*. It wasn't absolutely necessary, but it certainly was helpful. That device is no longer available, but there is a free app for Apple or Android devices! Just search for "The Focus Tool" in your app store, download it, and get to work!

The Focus Tool™ alerts you randomly throughout your day to bring your attention back to the present. It is easy to relax in a favorite chair, read a self-help book, and nod in agreement with what you are reading. It is something else to actually take those concepts and apply them during the stresses of everyday life.

Especially during the integration period after a big psychedelic healing journey, it can be all too easy to be swept away in surging emotional states. The Focus Tool™ works beautifully to help keep bringing you back into the moment with handy reminders of what is most important for you to remember.

Please, enjoy the use of The Focus Tool™ app free of charge for the basic version, which functions exactly like the original Focus Tool did.

— Shannon

"Buddha taught that one moment of total awareness is one moment of freedom and enlightenment. *Present Moment Awareness* clearly and succinctly provides us with authentic tools, exercises, reflections, and practices to access the awakened heart and mind inherent in us all."

— Lama Surya Das, author of *Awakening the Buddha Within*

"Shannon Duncan has taken major concepts from ancient traditions and modern psychology and distilled them into an easy-to-understand guide to awareness. His book makes these often nebulous and difficult to understand concepts available to anyone desiring personal and spiritual growth."

— Roger Jahnke, OMD, author of *The Healer Within*

"In the tradition of contemplative experience from all great sages, Shannon Duncan gives us a primer for greater awareness in our lives.... To be who we are is the point of life. This book is wonderful help in achieving that goal."

— Brother Wayne Teasdale, author of *The Mystic Heart*

"Like taking a mini-spiritual retreat, this exhilarating read, with doable exercises for challenging your beliefs, has you rediscovering yourself in the timelessness of the now. It sets you free to live the truly good life."

— Marcella Bakur Weiner, Ph.D., author/editor of
Psychotherapy and Religion: Many Paths, One Journey

Also by Shannon Duncan

Present Moment Awareness:
A Simple Step-by-Step Guide to Living in the Now

My first book, *Present Moment Awareness*, is being released in a new edition for its 20th anniversary. It has been given some needed updates and has modernized the usage of the "Focus Tool." For those just getting started on their path of healing and personal growth, I believe it to be a very useful companion to *Coming Full Circle*. It's a clear, simple guide to help build important understandings and self-awareness.

— Shannon

Ingram Content Group UK Ltd.
Milton Keynes UK
UKHW012246150323
418612UK00004B/205